P9-EMC-709

BENEDICT ARNOLD

Traitor to his Country

January 14, 1741—June 12, 1801

From early boyhood, Benedict Arnold was obsessed by dreams of wealth. He fought his way to prosperity and became the owner of a fleet of trading ships. When the King's taxes became oppressive, Arnold joined the Continental Army, not to save his country but to save his ships. Though his motives were selfish, he became one of the great heroes of the Revolution, then Commander of West Point. Embittered by rumors that he became rich at public expense, and still greedy for money, Arnold secretly switched allegiance to Britain and agreed to reveal information leading to the capture of West Point.

Books by
Jeannette Covert Nolan

ABRAHAM LINCOLN

ANDREW JACKSON

BENEDICT ARNOLD
Traitor to his Country

DOLLEY MADISON

FLORENCE NIGHTINGALE

THE GAY POET
The Story of Eugene Field

GEORGE ROGERS CLARK
Soldier and Hero

JOHN BROWN

LA SALLE AND THE GRAND ENTERPRISE

THE LITTLE GIANT
Stephen A. Douglas

O. HENRY
The Story of William Sidney Porter

SPY FOR THE CONFEDERACY
Rose O'Neal Greenhow

THE STORY OF CLARA BARTON OF THE RED CROSS

TREASON AT THE POINT

THE SHOT HEARD ROUND THE WORLD
The Story of Lexington and Concord

BENEDICT ARNOLD

TRAITOR TO HIS COUNTRY

Jeannette Covert Nolan

JULIAN MESSNER
NEW YORK

Published simultaneously in the United States and Canada by Julian Messner, a division of Simon & Schuster, Inc., 1 West 39 Street, New York, N.Y. 10018.

Ninth Printing, 1967

Printed in the United States of America
Library of Congress Catalog Card No. 56–10452

For
Evelyn R. Sickels

CONTENTS

THE PROPHECY OF THE INDIAN CHIEFTAIN, NATANIS:

"The Dark Eagle comes to claim the wilderness. The wilderness will yield to the Dark Eagle, but the Rock will defy him. The Dark Eagle will soar aloft to the sun. Nations will behold him and sound his praises. Yet when he soars highest his fall is most certain. When his wings brush the sky, then the arrow will pierce his heart."

1

SUMMER HOMECOMING, 1759

AT THE CROSSROADS, BENEDICT ARNOLD STOPPED AND SAT DOWN in the sun-warmed grass. He was not lost or confused. He knew the way to Norwich. But it was early evening; he had been walking steadily, stubbornly, all day. He was tired.

He remembered something his sister Hannah once had said: "Isn't it funny that the distance you have to travel getting to a place, any place, always seems much longer than the same distance coming back?"

Funny? Benedict didn't think so. It wasn't true, either. Hannah was mistaken.

For instance, his journey northward three months ago hadn't seemed long. The newly recruited Connecticut militiamen were starting off in the fine spring weather to join the English king's war against the French and Indians. Fifes had squealed and drums rolled. Excitement was in the air, and Benedict had felt his heart pound madly as he fell into the marching line.

Hannah had begged him not to go. In a very undignified manner she had pulled at his sleeve, the tail of his jacket.

"It's so far," she wailed. "Hundreds of miles!"

He had pushed her aside. "Don't fret, Hannah. Don't *cry!*"

"I wish Father hadn't given you permission to enlist! I suppose you've made up your mind, nothing could keep you from going?"

"Yes," he said, "I've made up my mind."

"And perhaps this is better than to have you leave without even telling us—as you did last year."

Of course it was better. Last year he'd been a runaway, going only as far as Hartford and sent home from there in disgrace, like a naughty baby. This year he was eighteen, strong, husky, and he had his father's permission.

"Good-by, Hannah," he said firmly. "I won't even bother to count the miles."

Coming back, though, he had counted them—every single one of the dismal miles; the days and days of tramping alone through forest and field; the nights of sleeping in whatever shelter he could find, in wilderness depths where wolves and panthers prowled, under hedges and haystacks, in barn lofts where mice skittered and sang their chattering songs. . . .

But he wouldn't think of all that now! He was in Connecticut, almost in sight of his own village, his own people, his father and mother and Hannah. They weren't expecting him; he would surprise them.

"And they'll be so glad to see me they won't ask too many questions," he said to himself.

He heard the clop-clop of horses, the creak of wheels, behind him and got to his feet. A big farm cart loaded with sacks of grain was approaching, headed toward Norwich. As he wondered whether to hail it and beg a ride, the driver drew rein and called to him.

"Going to town?"

"Yes, sir."

"So am I." The man moved over on the narrow seat. "Hop in."

Benedict hopped in. It would be perfectly safe, he thought; the man was a stranger to him.

The cart jolted and jogged on the rutted road.

"Been hot today," the man said. "Heat wave, uncommon for June, eh?"

"Yes, sir. Hot and dusty."

"Reckon you live in Norwich?"

"My parents live there. I've been up north, in New York, Lake George."

"Lake George?" The man whistled. "That *is* north. Nigh on to Canada! That's where the war is, the French and English scrapping over the forts. Lots of our colonial soldiers, too; some from right around here. Did you see any fighting?"

"I saw some of our American troops in camp, but no battles."

"You weren't in the army?"

"No." Benedict hesitated. "I was—working. I got a letter from my sister saying that my mother is sick."

"So you quit the job? Was it farm work?"

"Yes," Benedict answered faintly.

"I'm a farmer myself."

Benedict nodded and was silent. He would have liked to tell the man his name, for he was proud of it. He wanted to say boldly: "I'm Benedict Arnold. It's my father's name, too. My father is a selectman of Norwich, a merchant with a fleet of sailing ships that ply between the New England coast and the West Indies." He might have said that his grandfather, also named Benedict Arnold, had been an honored member of the Rhode Island Assembly, and his great-grandfather, the first Benedict Arnold in America, had succeeded the famed Roger Williams as president of Rhode Island Colony.

He was proud of his family and sometimes talked about it. But now he said nothing of this kind. Silence was wiser, he thought.

The man went on to speak of the war, how the conflict between France and England in Europe had spread to the outposts of both nations in America, with the Indians aiding the French forces, and the English colonists supporting their king.

"It just shows what we can do," the man said. "We can raise and train soldiers with the best of them. And officers. Like the Virginian, Colonel George Washington."

"Washington? Yes, he's a fine officer."

"As fine as ever stood in shoe leather!" The man clucked to his team. "Oh, we'll lick the Frenchies, Injuns and all!"

Benedict was watching the road. "I hate the French," he said.

"You do? Why?"

"They're our enemies, aren't they?"

"Yes, but I reckon, at that, they're no different from the people of other countries, some good, some bad. And it's not the people who make a war. It's their rulers, kings and princes; anyway, that's how it is with this one. Me, what I hate is *war*. Well, maybe when England wins in Canada, we'll have a spell of peace. I hope so!"

Benedict thought of the war. He did not hate it. Often in imagination he had seen himself clad in a glittering uniform, flourishing a magnificent sword, rushing into battle, followed by a band of valiant fellows who admired him and obeyed his every command. Why had there been nothing like that in the northern camps? No glory, only dreariness and dull chores. He had wanted action, not drudgery. He had felt bored and cheated. He loved his mother dearly and had been dismayed to learn she was ill. But secretly he knew that Hannah's letter had provided him with the excuse for doing something he already had determined to do.

The cart jogged, the driver talked ramblingly. Benedict was not listening. As they neared the village, he said abruptly: "I'll get out here."

"I'd as lief take you clear into town."

"No, thanks." The team slowed and he jumped down. "I'm obliged to you for the ride, sir."

The man clapped his reins and waved amiably. "So long," he said. "Giddap!"

Dusk was thick in the quiet streets. Lamps glowed in the windows of houses and shops, making a quilted pattern of light and shadow. Everything looked familiar to Benedict:

the fenced yards, the tavern with its tin sign swaying in the slight breeze, the church framed by arching elm trees. He walked briskly, dodging from one darker patch to the next. Then he faltered. He was just passing the drugshop of the Lathrop Brothers—and there stood Mr. Joshua Lathrop, one of the proprietors, directly in his path.

Mr. Lathrop, a bulky figure in powdered wig, spectacles and tight-buttoned coat, was a cousin to Benedict's mother.

"Ha!" he exclaimed now, peering through his spectacles. "Ha, it's you, is it?"

Benedict had never been fond of Mr. Joshua Lathrop, or of his brother Dr. Daniel Lathrop. He said, "Yes, sir."

"Well, bless my soul! Discharged from the military because of your poor mother, eh?"

Benedict said nothing. Let Mr. Lathrop think so, if it pleased him.

"And high time you ceased playing the young fool! You can finish your apprenticeship with me. We'll teach you the drug business, Daniel and I. You were just getting the hang of it last spring when you skipped off with the soldiers."

"I didn't skip, sir."

Mr. Lathrop grunted. "Perhaps not, but we won't split hairs. You can't deny that you have a reputation for mischief and pranks, many of them quite wicked and harmful. However, I'm willing to hire you again, in spite of it."

"Very good of you, sir."

"For your mother's sake, not yours. I know your mother would like you to settle down, as a decent lad should. You're smart enough, and not lazy. But you've always felt too big for your britches."

Suddenly Benedict was angry. He had no wish to continue the conversation, certainly none to be Mr. Lathrop's apprentice. The drug business? He detested it. He'd rather be in prison than in that stuffy shop. He detested criticism of any sort. He detested Mr. Lathrop, the fat old toad, the interfering old fuss-budget!

He said, "Your pardon, sir. Do not detain me. I'm in a hurry tonight."

"Tomorrow, then, we'll make some plans."

"If I am at leisure—"

"If *you're* at leisure? Ha! Tomorrow," Mr. Lathrop repeated. "Well, trot on. And my regards to your dear mother. Poor lady, so patiently bearing her burdens."

Brushing by, quickening his pace, Benedict thought: Burdens? What burdens? What's wrong? . . .

He was breathless when he reached the house. The front door was closed, but the glow of candles in the hall filtered out through the fanlight. He noticed that the white paint was peeling off the panels—why was that? It was a large handsome door; the whole house was large and handsome, and repainted every summer. Why should it look shabby and neglected this summer?

Frowning, he turned the knob and stepped inside and saw Hannah, just emerging from the kitchen into the hall. She was carrying a tray covered with a linen napkin.

"Hannah," he said.

"Benedict!" she gasped, and set the tray on a chair, then darted to throw her arms around his neck. "Oh, *Benedict!*"

"Hey, you're choking me!" Laughing, he freed himself. "Are you surprised?"

"I'm *amazed.*"

He kissed her plump pink cheek. "And glad?"

"Very glad. Mother will be, too. I'm taking some supper to her."

"Is she upstairs, Hannah?"

"Yes, in her bedroom. Father is with her."

"I got your letter telling me she was sick. That's why I came," Benedict said. "Is it—serious?"

"I'm afraid it is. Dr. Daniel Lathrop seems to think so." Hannah paused, her blue eyes misted with tears. "But I didn't tell you to come. I never dreamed you *could.* How did it happen—"

He interrupted. "I'll go right up to Mother's room."

"No, no," Hannah said. "Not until you've washed a bit. You're dirty as a pig, Benedict. Wait, I'll fetch you soap and water. Oh, I can scarcely believe you're here! I'm sure you'll help more than all the doctor's medicines."

He waited while she went for the washbowl and a towel.

It was pleasant, he thought, to be at home again—with Hannah to fetch him things.

2

CONVERSATION BY MOONLIGHT

AT SEVEN O'CLOCK BENEDICT WAS IN THE KITCHEN HAVING A second dish of cherry pudding. He had eaten a good supper of crisply fried bacon, baked beans and brown bread, but he was still hungry. He felt as though he had been hungry for months; and nothing had ever tasted half so delicious as this fruit pudding in its sweetened juice.

He had the kitchen all to himself. Hannah was tidying his mother's room for the night; his father had gone out. When he finished his pudding, Benedict rested his elbows on the table and thought about his parents. It seemed to him they had changed a great deal.

Of course, he had known that his mother might be changed; weeks of fever and pain would have done that. He would never forget how small and frail she had looked in the big bed, as he went into her room and knelt beside her.

She had always been a very religious woman, reading the Bible every night—and tonight, too; as she greeted him, she kept her finger in the book to mark the page. She was weak and couldn't talk much; but she had smiled at him and stroked his rough dark hair, and they had prayed together.

He hadn't said, "Mother, forgive me for causing you anxiety." There was no need to say it. As he rose from his knees and bent to kiss her, he knew she loved and forgave him.

But the change in his father was more puzzling. His father was pale, his shoulders stooped; he seemed to have shrunk in height and withered, like an old, old man.

"Are you quite well, sir, Benedict had said.

"Yes, in excellent health," Mr. Arnold answered. "Welcome home, my son. Welcome home."

Afterward, at supper, Benedict had observed that his father had no appetite, that the ruffles of lace at his throat and wrists were frayed.

"Why do you stare at me, son?" Mr. Arnold had demanded.

Embarrassed, Benedict had glanced away; and Hannah had begun to speak nervously of affairs in the neighborhood and the village.

Now Hannah bustled into the kitchen with a swish of long skirts, her blond curls bobbing under a frilled cap.

"You've grown, sis," Benedict said teasingly. "You'll soon be as tall as I am."

"I'm two inches taller, and you know it." She tossed her head. "A year younger and two inches taller."

He grinned, thinking she was a very pretty girl; but he wouldn't tell her so, it might make her vain. "You're sassy," he said. "Sassy as a jay bird."

Hannah whisked the empty dish from the table. "My lands, Benedict, you've eaten *all* the pudding! *You'll* soon be doubled over with stomach-ache. Where's Father?"

"He went out; he said he'd walk down to the wharves. Is one of his ships arriving?"

"No. He's been unlucky with his ships recently."

"Unlucky?"

"Storms at sea," Hannah said. "Benedict, Mother is sleeping peacefully. Let's go and sit in the yard, and I'll tell you."

They went out to a bench in the yard. The night was beautiful, with a full moon silvering trees, bushes and rooftops. In low tones, Hannah told him about their father's troubles. Several of his trading vessels had been either crippled or totally wrecked by storms, valuable cargoes of merchandise had sunk to the bottom of the ocean.

"He hadn't the money to pay his bills," Hannah said. "He borrowed money and now the men he borrowed from are clamoring to be repaid."

Benedict recalled that Mr. Lathrop had spoken of his mother as a "poor lady." He asked, "Do you mean we're poor, Hannah?"

"I guess we are. Oh, not starving poor. Father still has two ships, but they can't be sailed until they're repaired."

"He must repair them!"

"I'm afraid he won't. He's awfully discouraged. Every thing has come at once. And nowadays," Hannah said slowly, "he's spending the little money we have and most of his time at the tavern—drinking."

Benedict was shocked. He pictured his father loitering among the shiftless crowd that frequented the tavern, associating with idlers and drunkards—a drunkard himself. This was terrible! No wonder Mr. Lathrop said Mrs. Arnold was a poor lady, with burdens to bear! Benedict felt ashamed for his father, ashamed that his mother should be pitied by Mr. Lathrop, perhaps by the whole village.

"I know why Father likes to go to the tavern," Hannah was saying. "It's a relief from his worries—about Mother and about you. He's just stopped *trying,* Benedict. And that only makes the debts and the worries bigger."

"I'll never waste my time in taverns!" Benedict declared grimly, angrily. "I'll earn money, piles of it! When I'm Father's age I'll be rich!"

"Oh, rich—that's not important."

"Hannah, are you crazy? Of course it is!"

"I'd rather you'd be honest and respected, always do your duty."

"I'll be those things, too."

"Well, you can be whatever you want," Hannah said. "But you have a streak of selfishness in your nature—"

"I have not!"

"Yes, sometimes you're almost cruelly selfish. You hurt people, deceive them."

"Don't!" he said. "Don't scold me, Hannah. Anyway, I've never deceived you. I couldn't!"

She stared off into the moonlight, twisting her cap strings. Then she bent toward him and whispered: "You're not a deserter–are you?"

"A deserter?" he cried, infinitely startled. "No, Hannah! No, no!"

She sighed and smiled, as if a dreadful weight had been lifted from her heart. "I shouldn't have asked you that."

"Well, why did you? Why should you think of it?"

"It was in the paper," she said.

"What! In what paper? When?"

"The *New York Gazette,* last month. Dr. Lathrop's paper. It slipped out of his pocket one day, I picked it up and read it."

"What did the paper say, Hannah?"

"Oh, just that some men had deserted from the camp at Lake George, and that a reward had been posted for their arrest. One was described as young and short in stature, dark complexioned, blue eyed, with a hawklike profile. Somehow I was reminded of you. And tonight, when you came in—well, for a minute I was scared. Wasn't that silly of me?"

"Very, very silly." He laughed hoarsely. "Did Father see the paper? Or Mother?"

"No, I burned it with other trash."

"Did you mention it to anybody? Anybody at all?"

"No, and it was never mentioned to me. I think the doctor is the only person in Norwich who subscribes to the *Gazette.* But suppose the description was seen, who would connect it with you? Everyone knows how you nagged at Father until he simply had to consent to your going with the militia. Deserters are cowards. Everyone knows you're not a coward."

Benedict was thinking rapidly. Probably Dr. Daniel Lathrop did not read his New York paper item by item; he was a busy man. At any rate, it seemed that his suspicions had not been aroused by the printed description of a youthful deserter. And if, indeed, he was the only Norwich subscriber to the *Gazette,* there was little likelihood that anyone else would ever read it.

People in villages do gossip, and sometimes it's an advantage—isn't it? By tomorrow evening the story would be all around the streets that Benedict Arnold had been discharged from the army. Mr. Joshua Lathrop would say so, for it was what he believed. He had taken the discharge for granted. Before the week was out, everybody would be believing and saying it—exactly as everybody knew that Benedict Arnold was mischievous, prankish, reckless, but never a coward.

A month has gone by, Benedict thought. There's no danger now. Not if I'm cautious, meek and mild. And I can be! Cautious as a fox, meek as Moses, mild as milk. . . .

"With both of our parents to care for, we'll have plenty of responsibilities," Hannah was saying gravely. "I'll manage the housekeeping."

"And I'll paint the house. I don't like the way it looks, all soiled and scaly. I want it to look nice and trim—"

"But you'll have to do something to earn money, Benedict. You must hunt for a job."

"Hunt?" he said. "When it's known that I want work, people will come hunting *me.* I met Mr. Lathrop outside the drugshop tonight. He asked me to be his apprentice again."

"Oh, good!"

"But I don't intend to."

"Why not? It's an opportunity," Hannah said. "The Lathrops are very generous."

"Dr. Daniel may be generous. Mr. Joshua is an ancient penny-pinching crank—and the one who'd pay my wages."

"Oh, dear, I wish you weren't so hard on everybody, Benedict! Anyway, the wages would be *regular.* And I really think that when you first went to the drugshop Father made a contract with the Lathrops. You'll have to serve out your time there."

"I suppose I'm trapped then."

"Trapped? Don't feel like that about it."

He saw that she was distressed, and he was sorry for her. "I'll talk to Mr. Joshua," he said. "And one thing you can depend on. I'll always take care of *you,* Hannah."

"I'm sure you will."

"I want you to remember it."

"I'll remember," she said.

He had difficulty getting to sleep that night. The moon was too bright, his thoughts too muddled. What a state of things he had come home to! His mother ill, his father's affairs so unsettled—and all of Norwich knowing, pitying, probably scorning the Arnolds.

And the notice in the paper—A deserter?

Well, if he was a deserter it wasn't his fault. They hadn't treated him fairly in the army. They'd never given him the chance to prove he could be a soldier, and a good one. Why wouldn't he have slipped away?

"It was somebody else's fault, not mine!" he murmured, and this was soothing to him.

He said it over and over, until at last he slept.

3

THE DRUG CLERK

BENEDICT'S MOTHER DIED ON AUGUST 15 OF THAT SAME HOT, dry summer. Her death was mourned not only by her husband and children, but by the entire community, where she had been beloved for her gentle disposition and many deeds of charity. In that sad time, hundreds of friends and neighbors flocked to the Arnold house with gifts of flowers and words of sympathy.

"Your mother was a saint on earth," they said to Benedict and Hannah. "Now she is an angel in heaven."

And they said what a blessing it was that Benedict should have been with her in the last weeks of her life. "You were a comfort to her, lad," they said, "for she had missed you sorely."

Benedict knew this was true. Grieving deeply and sincerely, he held fast to the thought that by coming home he had made his mother happy. If at first he had been doubtful about his decision, he now did not regret it. No, everything had turned out for the best. The people of Norwich all seemed to be convinced that he had been honorably discharged from the militia. By the end of the summer, he was almost convinced of it himself.

There were a few hours when he still felt uneasy. One day in the autumn a recruiting officer passed through the village. Benedict had just a glimpse of him, and recognized him as a fellow he had seen before, in the north. But he did not speak to him to renew their acquaintance. Instead, he ducked into a convenient stable and hid in a harness closet. Several days later the officer reappeared; again Benedict retreated to the harness closet. It was not a cozy spot—he tore his shirt on a rusty nail and got cobwebs in his hair—but it was quiet and dim.

He heard next day that the recruiting officer had inquired whether any deserters had fled to Norwich—and that the villagers had not been cordial to him. The fact was that people were no longer concerned with such matters. The novelty and excitement of the war had worn off. More and more the colonists were thinking that it was the King's war, not theirs. Some leaders in America were even complaining aloud of England's unfairness to the colonies, requiring them to furnish troops for the conquest of Canada, yet taxing them so heavily. From now on, they would have less and less enthusiasm for the war—and for the King, too. The colonies were expanding, gathering a strength of their own, beginning to resent the dictates of a greedy monarch on a foreign throne.

One of the relatives who came to the funeral of Benedict's mother was Captain Oliver Arnold of New Haven. Captain Oliver was Benedict's uncle, a brother of Mr. Arnold of Norwich. He talked to Mr. Arnold about moving to New Haven.

"It's a thriving town," he said. "Five thousand inhabitants, most of them prosperous. Yale College is there. Wouldn't you like for Benedict to be a student at Yale College? And you could go into the shipping business with me; I'm doing very well. And Hannah could find a nice beau and get married!"

Mr. Arnold smiled, but shook his head. "No, Oliver. This is the place for me. I must stay here."

Captain Oliver was stout and bluff, red faced and forthright. "Why?" he said. "Why must you stay? I can't see any future for you in Norwich. Move to New Haven and get a fresh start."

But Mr. Arnold merely smiled—and Benedict, listening, knew that the arguments made no impression on him at all.

As Hannah had said, he was utterly discouraged; he lacked the energy to try a fresh start at anything, anywhere.

"Benedict, your father is a sick man," Captain Oliver said afterward to his nephew. "Sick in mind and spirit, if not in body. I fear he may never improve. A difficult situation for you and Hannah. Do you think you're equal to it?"

"Yes, sir."

Benedict was stanch, but regretful. He would have liked to be educated at Yale College, for he had always liked school. As a small boy he had been sent to Dr. Jewett's school in near-by Montville, and at eleven he had gone on to the town of Canterbury to study with Dr. James Cogswell, a noted New England scholar. At both schools he had distinguished himself as an apt pupil. Latin and mathematics were his favorite subjects; he had learned a little French and Greek, also, and a great deal of English grammar.

Why had he dropped out of school at the age of fifteen? He couldn't exactly remember now. Some sudden foolish whim, probably, in which his parents indulged him. From childhood he had possessed a fierce, flashing temper—and, according to Norwich folk, his father couldn't discipline him and his mother petted and spoiled him.

Now, in these vexing times, he was often sorry he hadn't remained at Canterbury. I might have prepared for college, he thought bitterly. I might have been something more worth while than a drug clerk!

For that, it seemed, was what he was destined to be—apprentice in the Lathrops' drugshop.

"Yes," Mr. Joshua had said, "there's a contract to fulfill."

So, reluctantly, he went to work for the old toad.

He brought his first week's wages home to Hannah. A handful of shillings; he laid them in her lap.

"Oh, Mr. Joshua *is* being generous," she said. "It's more than he paid you before."

"He's working me harder than before."

"Are you pleased with the position, Benedict?"

Position? He wouldn't have called it that, and he was not pleased. But what a dear creature Hannah was!—working constantly herself, like a little Trojan, cooking, cleaning, tending the house and an ailing father, doing all so cheerfully and capably. He smiled and patted her hand.

"You don't hear me grumbling, do you?" he said. "The shop isn't too awfully bad."

No, really, it was not bad. As the weeks and the months passed, he was not too discontented there. Each day was twelve hours long, but rolled by swiftly. Mr. Lathrop had genial moods as well as crotchety, and had been known to praise his clerk for skill in mixing tonics, salves and lotions. Frequently Benedict had the nice feeling of being clever and appreciated.

The shop was spacious and bright and smelled delightfully of licorice and cinnamon. The two large bay windows in front were decorated with beautifully shaped bottles of blown glass containing colored water, ruby red, turquoise blue and emerald green, which sparkled brilliantly as they reflected the sunshine. Broad counters and tiers of shelves displayed a great variety of wares; for, besides medicine, Mr. Lathrop sold tea, coffee, spices, herbs, perfumes, chocolate and rock candy; needles, pins and sealing wax and dozens of other useful articles. And he sold books, most of which he imported from London.

These books fascinated Benedict; he loved books of any sort, even books of poetry. When not busy wrapping up purchases, or helping with mortar and pestle in the drug room, he would take a book from the shelves, open it and soon be absorbed in reading. If the volume was particularly elegant, bound in soft leather and illustrated with engravings, he yearned to buy it. But he hadn't the money for such luxuries now.

"Sometime I'll be rich and have a huge library of books," he said to Hannah.

"Oh, don't gabble so much about riches!" she exclaimed. "It's not the proper ambition for a boy."

"It's my ambition—one of mine," he retorted, making a face at her. "And don't you *preach!*"

Of his two employers, Benedict preferred Dr. Daniel Lathrop, though he saw him less often. Sometimes he went to the doctor's house for dinner, or rode on errands for him, sitting erect as a ramrod in the doctor's grand chaise, which was adorned with the Lathrop coat of arms and many rows of brass studding. It was the most aristocratic equipage in Norwich, perhaps in all Connecticut. Rattling over the cobbles, Benedict would pretend that it belonged to him and the doctor was his guest.

Sometimes people came to the shop with cuts or bruises or broken bones to be expertly bandaged. Occasionally Dr. Lathrop let Benedict do the bandaging, while he stood by to supervise.

"You have the knack, Benedict," he once said. "The knack for adjusting splints. I'm not saying you're a surgeon—mustn't get that into your head. But with sufficient practice, you might be."

By the day's end Benedict was usually weary, but restless. When the shop was locked for the night, he would go home to supper with Hannah and his father, then strike out for a solitary walk through the town.

His wanderings led him to the wharves. At Norwich the Yantic and the Shetucket rivers merge to form the Thames. From there the Thames River flows wide and deep to Fishers Island Sound, and on to the Atlantic Ocean. Along the waterfront stretched the low gray wharves flanked by warehouses, and moored at anchor were boats ranging in size from humble skiffs and dories to towering merchant ships. The air was fragrant with tar, turpentine and sawed trees.

Benedict loved boats; the sea enticed him. Years ago he had made a voyage with his father to the West Indies; every detail of it was still vivid in his memory. He had examined the vessel from stem to stern, poking and prying, until he felt that he knew all about it and could have sailed it himself. The crew had been amused by him—Mr. Arnold's little black-haired jackanapes, who already had muscles like wire and the agility of a cat. They showed him how to climb to the masthead, grab a backstay and slide to the deck. They applauded when he spun a series of handsprings for them, or shinnied up a rope like greased lightning. They nicknamed him "Matey" and "Commodore" and "Admiral." He was a sailor, born and bred, they said.

He strutted and capered. "Yes, yes! I'm your boss!"

"Aye, aye, sir," the men replied, roaring with laughter.

That was the only one of the Arnold ships at any dock now, and in another month it would be sold at auction. Mr. Arnold's debts were enormous; perhaps some of them would never be paid—for he would never go to sea again. Since his wife's death, he scarcely even ventured from his chair.

"And how can he endure it?" Benedict muttered. "Why can't Father rouse himself?"

From the riverbank, Benedict would saunter to the gristmill and think of the day he had astounded the village by whirling dizzily on the blade of the windmill. He had gone to the mill with a bag of grain to be ground; the revolving blades seemed to hypnotize him and as one came level with his shoulder he grasped it. Up, up he was swept, above the earth, the mill—then down, down, plunged into the icy bath of the pond, then upward and around and down, the water frothing over his head.

As if by magic a crowd had collected. People screamed that he would be slashed to pieces, drowned. Grinning, he clung to the blade. Around and around he went, dipping into the pond, then out. When he'd had enough, he slipped off and bowed to his gaping audience.

He was half frozen, wet, and much gratified by the sensation he had caused. The miller was furious.

And here was the village green and the old cannon he once had investigated—to everybody's consternation. The cannon wasn't just old; it was antique. He had often wondered whether it could be made to shoot.

Well, why not find out?

One placid Sabbath morning, when everybody was at church, he went to the green, pointed the cannon's muzzle skyward, poured in a horn of powder, thrust in a blazing torch.

Bang!

The constable chased him, yelling frantically: "You limb of Satan! You young fiend!"

Benedict was a bit deafened by the explosion; his hair and eyebrows were singed. But he outran the constable.

They were foes, anyway, Benedict and the constable—they had been ever since Thanksgiving Day, which Norwich had celebrated by lighting bonfires on the hills surrounding the village. Benedict had wanted his bonfire to be the biggest, so he had gone to the shipyards and stolen a barrel of tar. He had the barrel almost up the hill when the constable overtook him.

"Stop, thief! Stop!"

Benedict had ripped off his jacket and dared the constable to fight.

"Come on. I dare you!"

The constable said he didn't fight minnows like Benedict Arnold. He got the barrel and retired—with the mocking laughter of the minnow ringing in his ears.

Somehow, these evening walks were consoling to Benedict. His present life was not at all to his fancy, but his boyhood had been exciting, and surely the future would be, too.

Hannah believed, didn't she, that her brother could be whatever he wanted to be? Yes, and she was right about it! The main thing was to *know* what he wanted, to chart a course—and then let nothing stand in his way!

4

NEW VENTURE

DURING THE NEXT TWO YEARS MR. ARNOLD FAILED STEADILY IN health. Though everything possible was done for him, he seemed to have no wish to live; and in 1761, he died quietly and was laid to rest in the village churchyard.

Benedict was twenty then and had completed his apprenticeship with Mr. Lathrop. The idea of leaving Norwich had been in his mind ever since his Uncle Oliver had spoken to him about it. He began to make some definite plans.

"We're going to move to New Haven, Hannah," he announced one evening as his sister sat sewing by the light of the parlor lamp.

She looked up, wide eyed. "Move?"

"Yes. I told Mr. Lathrop, and I must say he was sorry to hear it. I think he'd like to keep me in the shop until I'm as rusty and old as he is."

"Why are we going?" Hannah asked.

"Because I could never be satisfied here. The people aren't friendly. They think we're poor and don't amount to much."

"Oh, nonsense, Benedict! That's silly. Everyone has been kinder than kind to us."

"To you, maybe. Not to me. I haven't a real friend in the town."

"Do you want my opinion?" Hannah said. "To have a friend, you've got to be one. It's not that Norwich people aren't friendly. It's *you.*"

Scowling, he paced the length of the room. He wouldn't quarrel with Hannah, but he was irritated. She should not presume to lecture him.

"In New Haven I'll have my own drugshop," he said.

"Father willed this house to us both; it's all we have. I'm selling it to Mr. Hugh Ledlie."

Hannah put down her sewing. Her hands were trembling. "You've sold the house?"

"I've agreed to sell it six months from now; but Mr. Ledlie is paying me in advance so that I can journey to London—"

"London!"

"To buy the stock for my business. You'll occupy the house in my absence. When I'm established in New Haven, I'll come for you."

"So it's arranged?" she said. "But I like Norwich, Benedict."

"You'll like New Haven better. You'll think my plan is splendid, once you get used to it."

Hannah sighed. "I had thought we'd live always in our dear old house, our dear old village." Then her eyes brightened. "Why don't you go to New Haven—and I'll stay here."

"Alone? Ridiculous!" he said. "You know I wouldn't. What would you do without me? A maid of nineteen, no means of supporting yourself, no relatives near—and no money."

He paused. There *was* something she might do without him; the mere idea of it angered him. Probably he ought to quiz her about it so that she would know precisely how he felt. He drew up a chair and sat beside her. "I have something to say to you, Hannah."

"Yes?" she murmured, and she was blushing, her cheeks as red as peonies, her eyes downcast.

"Last Sunday you were escorted home from church by a young scapegrace who's recently come to Norwich as a dancing master."

"A young gentleman, Benedict. His name is Louis—"

"Don't tell me his name. I don't want to know it. I know all that's necessary. He's a Frenchman."

"French by birth," Hannah said. "He has taken up residence in Connecticut."

"Oh, a turncoat, a renegade? Well, you're not to see him again."

Hannah lifted her head. "Not—not see him again?"

"I won't have him pursuing and annoying my sister."

"He doesn't pursue and annoy me, Benedict."

"Of course he does! You're quibbling. I hate Frenchmen. I won't have you walking out in public with one. I forbid it!"

"But what a foolish prejudice," Hannah said. "The French are no longer our enemies. The King's war with them has been won."

"This fellow is an unsuitable companion for you—"

"But why? He's honest and respectable."

"I shall be the judge of that!" His temper flaring, Benedict got up. He kicked at his chair and it fell with a crash to the floor. "I warn you, Hannah. You're to have nothing more to do with your cheap little dancing master. If you do—"

"Yes?" she said. "Yes?"

"I shall be obliged to take the sternest measures against him."

"Measures? What do you mean?"

"Disobey me and you'll know!"

She looked thoughtful. "You hate Louis for being French, a dancing master and what you call a turncoat. Not because he's interested in me? I don't believe it. If he were one of the village boys, I believe you'd still dislike him."

"Hush!" Benedict's voice shook with rage. "I am your brother, the head of the family now that Father's dead. It's my duty to protect you. I shall do so, whether or not you wish it. I tell you, you're not to see the Frenchman. Do you understand me, Hannah?"

"I understand you," she said. "I understand you very well."

He wasted no time in securing passage on a ship bound for England. In London he bought drugs, supplies and a great parcel of books. Then he explored the city. How immense and dingy it was, and how crammed with historical landmarks and monuments. He went to the theater, to the famous parks and gardens; he dined in coffeehouses and coaching inns. He saw castles and cathedrals, the palace in which King George III was living, Westminster Abbey where scores of English soldiers and heroes were buried.

His ancestors had been natives of Wales; in a London museum he was told that the name Arnold could be traced to an early English word meaning "honor."

Arnold—honor! He must tell Hannah. Oh, she had been obstinate and impudent, but she was only a girl, after all. He was devoted to her, he needed her—and would need her still more in New Haven. She would be his housekeeper there and also help him with his business. He said to himself that he would take her a present, something fashionable, a fan of ivory, sandalwood and ostrich plumes, or a bolt of flowered taffeta to make a gown and cape. He knew she had heeded his warning and forgotten that jigging French whippersnapper!

The westward voyage from England was serene, the weather clear. Benedict talked with the ship's officers; they were impressed by his knowledge of sailing and navigation.

"I deserve no credit," he said modestly. "It's in my blood. My father was a seafaring man—as I hope to be someday."

Back in America he went straight to Captain Oliver Arnold in New Haven.

"Advise me where to set up my shop, Uncle," he said. "I can't afford to buy a piece of property. I shall have to rent. I think, don't you, that a good location is important?"

"Very important," Captain Oliver answered. "We must look around for one."

With his uncle, Benedict spent several days inspecting storerooms that were vacant and might be rented. The one he found was in Chapel Street and smaller than he would have wished.

"But it will do temporarily," he said. "In a year or two I

shall build a big place in Water Street. I must lease a cottage here, too. Hannah will be anxious to come to her new home."

"You haven't seen Hannah since you left Norwich six months ago?"

"No, and it's time I gave up the house to Mr. Ledlie. I must not violate the terms of my agreement with Mr. Ledlie!"

"Or any agreement with anyone—ever," said bluff Captain Arnold. "That's the first precept for success in the world, my boy."

Benedict had the Chapel Street storeroom scoured and scrubbed, and furnished it with the London merchandise. A tinsmith made him a beautiful sign to be hung above the door. The sign was of black metal, with gleaming gilt letters:

B. ARNOLD
DRUGGIST, BOOKSELLER, &c.
FROM LONDON
SIBI TOTIQUE

When the sign was up, Captain Oliver Arnold came to see it.

"And what is the Latin inscription?" he asked. "I don't read Latin. *'Sibi Totique?'* A noble sentiment, probably. Translate it for me."

Glibly Benedict translated. "It's 'For himself and for all.' "

"Ah?" said Captain Arnold. "Ah, indeed?"

While he was getting his shop in readiness, Benedict was introduced to Eleazar Oswald, another young merchant of New Haven. Eleazar was intelligent and athletic; Benedict liked him. In the summer he invited Eleazar to go to Norwich with him.

"To fetch my sister Hannah," he said. "I wrote her that I'd be there soon, though I couldn't tell her the hour, or even the day, of my arrival."

Eleazar proposed that they ride horseback. "I have two horses. Returning, you can hire a coach for your sister and her luggage—girls always encumber themselves with such stacks of luggage! We can trail along behind the coach. Take your pistol; we'll have some target shooting on the road. How I wish I could ever beat you at it, Benedict! But I can't. You are a champion marksman."

Benedict bowed his thanks for the compliment and said he never traveled without a gun.

The ride to Norwich was pleasant. At nine o'clock of a warm, misty night, they were at the Arnold house, dismounting at the hitching-block. Benedict saw that the parlor was lighted and the window open. He touched Eleazar's arm.

"One moment," he whispered. "It may be that the minister and his wife, or some of the neighbors, are calling on my sister. I'll peep in."

Eleazar waited at the edge of the lawn. Benedict tiptoed to the parlor window and peeped beneath the curtains.

There were Hannah and the French dancing master seated together on the sofa, chatting gaily, like a pair of magpies!

Benedict was stunned. He rubbed his eyes and looked again.

Then he crossed the lawn to Eleazar.

"It's all right," he said, "but I've thought of a comical trick to play on my sister. Just as a lark, you know. You go to the front door, knock once, open the door and step in. Hannah will rush into the hall. She'll see you, a stranger, and be puzzled—until I follow you in."

"But she may be frightened," Eleazar said.

"Oh, no. She'll think it's funny. Go on!"

As Eleazar walked hesitantly to the door, Benedict quickly got his pistol from his saddle bags. He loaded, primed and cocked the pistol, and stationed himself at a point in the yard where he could see both the door and the window. Eleazar knocked once, rather timidly. Immediately Benedict shouted, "Hannah! Hannah, I'm home!"

In an instant a slender figure leaped from the window to the darkness beneath. It was the Frenchman. Benedict gave him time to rise, so that his head was outlined in the lamplight. Then Benedict fired—not at the Frenchman's head, but into the air.

Eleazar Oswald had not entered the house; he was hurrying toward Benedict—and the Frenchman was scampering down the street, vanishing in the distance.

"What is it?" Eleazar demanded. "What—"

"Wait out here for five minutes," Benedict said.

He strode into the parlor, where Hannah crouched in a corner of the sofa, her face hidden in her hands.

"Good evening, Sister."

"You shot him," Hannah moaned. "You've killed him."

"No. I could have killed him. Next time we meet, I will."

"There'll never be a next time. He's gone, he won't come back."

"I'm quite sure of that," Benedict said. "At the rate he was going, he must now be in the next county—your brave Louis. Get up, Hannah. Dry your tears. Pack your trunks and bags. We start for New Haven early in the morning."

She got to her feet. "Louis is a good young man. He wanted me to marry him."

Benedict laughed. "He's not a man at all. He's a mouse."

"Oh, how can you be so horrid, Benedict?"

"I'm not horrid. I warned you; apparently you didn't listen. Well, listen to this, Hannah. I have a friend with me. Eleazar Oswald, he's outside. When he comes in I shall tell him a fanciful yarn about this little fracas. I'll say it was a trick and you are to smile."

"Smile!"

"Don't say a word to contradict me. Not a word."

Hannah made a gesture of sorrowful despair. "What could I say? I'll never breathe a word of it to anyone. I would not humiliate you—as you have humiliated me."

5

THE YOUNG MERCHANT

BENEDICT BELIEVED IN ADVERTISING. WITH PRINTED HANDBILLS and in the newspapers he advertised the opening of his neat and artistic shop. His stock was widely assorted; he thought it would attract customers. Many wonderful wares were on his shelves, such as preserved fruit, figs, currants and tamarinds; painters' colors, wallpaper, maps and charts. To the ladies he offered jeweled buttons, chains and bracelets, earrings and watches. And for the Yale College students he had textbooks in Latin, Greek and French.

He also advertised his ability to mix medicines and to prescribe remedies for minor ailments; and when the people of New Haven referred to him as "Doctor" Arnold, he didn't correct them.

From the beginning, he prospered in the town.

Though not really handsome, he dressed exceptionally well. His waistcoats were embroidered; he wore lace ruffles, white silk stockings and silver-buckled shoes. He hadn't much humor in him, but his extensive reading made him a lively conversationalist at the Masonic Lodge, where he associated with New Haven's most prominent citizens. He liked social gatherings, danced gracefully and was a superb skater. At sports, or in any contest of strength, he excelled.

And he was absolutely fearless.

One day, as a herd of oxen was being driven through the streets, a maddened bull swung away and charged, snorting and bellowing, into a throng of people on the pavement. Men shouted and swore, women shrieked, frightened children dodged the lowered horns and great trampling hoofs.

The drover ran after the bull, but it tossed him into the gutter and plunged on, as if it could never be stopped.

Then Benedict Arnold was seen riding his horse full tilt, right at the bull, head on. Just as he would have collided with it, he pulled up short, leaned forward and with thumb and fingers caught the bull by its tender nostrils and squeezed the nostrils shut. The bull reared on hind legs, heaving and pawing, lashing its tail, struggling in vain to tear loose from that iron grip. Gradually it was quieter, and the drover came with a coil of rope to fasten around its neck.

For months the town talked about the subduing of the bull. It became a legend, a bit of folklore. And who else but Benedict Arnold would have known how—or dared—to do it? What pluck he had, what presence of mind!

In fact, he was a very unusual person, and so good to his sister, too. Though Miss Hannah sometimes worked in the shop, she was the mistress of a nice house and a servant. She had pretty clothes, stylish bonnets. She went regularly to church with "Doctor" Arnold, and often to teas and parties. Everyone remarked on his politeness to her.

"But you haven't got a beau yet, Hannah?" Captain Oliver Arnold was once to ask of her.

"No, Uncle," she said, smiling. "No beau. Not yet."

Now that the French and Indian War was over, many New England colonists were trading briskly with the Canadians, and soon Benedict engaged in this business. He bought horses in Connecticut and shipped them to Quebec where an agent sold them for him. With the money he received, he bought more horses and he made frequent trips to Canada himself, leaving the shop for Hannah to manage in his absence.

Sometimes he went by sea, sometimes by land. In this way he learned the geography of Canada, especially the eastern region around Quebec.

His business expanded and he bought a ship, the *Fortune,*

and sent it out to trade in the West Indies. Again he advertised.

"B. Arnold," said a notice in the *Connecticut Gazette*, "will transport cargoes of large, genteel, fat horses, pork, oats and hay, choice cotton and salt to the West Indies."

His vessel brought back to America casks of rum, barrels of sugar and molasses, which he sold at a profit. He bought two more ships, the *Sally* and the *Three Brothers*, and he said proudly to Hannah:

"Now I'm the owner of a fleet, just as Father was!"

But shipping conditions had changed since his father's day, taxes were much heavier. To avoid the taxes some American shipowners were sliding past the customs officials at the ports, without paying the fee which the English King demanded. This was smuggling; it was illegal; the King was determined to end it. England would teach her colonies a harsh lesson, and British troops would be distributed among them to see that the lesson was borne in mind. Also Americans would be further taxed to pay for the upkeep of these troops.

The colonists of course, protested against the new policies. They said that as British subjects they had certain inalienable rights which the king was ignoring. When a law was enacted requiring that a stamp be purchased and attached to all contracts, wills, mortgages and other papers, they protested so loudly that this Stamp Act was repealed. Still, in every village and town, there were people who felt that the increasing tyranny of the king's government must be defied—that perhaps a separation of the colonies from England was inevitable.

Benedict Arnold was one of these people, the leader of a group composed mostly of young and impulsive men. Benedict could see no justice in the oppressive trade laws—besides, they interfered with his business! He said that to disregard them was an evidence of patriotism, and he was an ardent patriot.

One cold January Saturday in 1766, Benedict had an angry argument with a sailor named Peter Boles, a member of the *Fortune*'s crew. Boles said he had not been paid all his wages for the latest voyage of the *Fortune.*

"You lie," Benedict said. "You're a scoundrel and you'll get no more money from me!"

When they parted, Boles went to the customhouse and asked to see the king's collector Mr. Sanford. A clerk told him that Mr. Sanford was out.

"You'll have to come on Monday," the clerk said. "Or perhaps I can attend to the matter?"

"No," Boles replied. "It's about a smuggler. I'll talk to Mr. Sanford Monday."

Sunday morning a friend reported to Benedict that Peter Boles intended to accuse him publicly of smuggling. Benedict knew where Boles lived in New Haven. He got a whip and went there. He thrashed Boles soundly and ordered him to leave town immediately.

"Yes, sir," Boles whimpered. "Yes, sir, I will!"

But on Monday Benedict glimpsed the sailor skulking near the customhouse. Waylaying him, Benedict forced him to sign a written confession that the Devil had inspired him to inform on the owner of the *Fortune.* Never again would he be such a lying scoundrel; he was leaving New Haven now, never to return.

Benedict was relieved—until that evening, when he heard that Boles was drinking in the tavern with a gang of noisy comrades. White faced with wrath, he stalked into the tavern, grabbed Boles by the collar and dragged him to the green in the center of town. Stripping the sailor of his shirt, he tied him to the whipping post and gave him forty strokes of the whip.

"Get out!" he cried. *"Get out!"*

Boles did not linger; he got out of New Haven, and for several days nothing was seen of him.

But a number of people had seen the second whipping;

they said that Benedict Arnold's behavior had been brutal, unwarranted—and not what might be expected from an innocent man. The town was in an uproar about it. Even Benedict's friends had been amazed by his violence. He was arrested, tried by a jury of his fellow citizens and fined fifty shillings.

Once more Peter Boles came to New Haven, this time to pocket the fine.

"It's absurd, outrageous!" Benedict exclaimed to Hannah, after the trial. "What have I done? Administered a little chastisement to a sniveling spy! I should be thanked for that!"

"The jury must have thought the chastisement was severe," Hannah suggested.

"Bah! The tongue of that whip is only a small cord. Boles is a worm to wince under it. I wish I'd used a leather thong on him!"

"There is a law, though, against smuggling, and you broke it, Benedict."

"I'll not admit that I broke it. But the majority of Connecticut merchants *are* breaking it, constantly. They have to—or be ruined. A silly law! If we're to be prosecuted for not observing it, half the shipowners in the colonies will land in jail. I've written a letter and sent it to be published in the *Gazette*. Here's a copy. Read it, Hannah."

The letter was bitterly sarcastic; it contrasted Benedict Arnold's honorable purposes with the villainy of spies like Peter Boles.

"Well, I don't know," Hannah murmured. "I want to believe you. And you'll never say that you may be wrong."

"My dear girl, I am never wrong."

"But if a thing *is* wrong, you can't make it otherwise just by saying so, can you? Even though you say it a hundred times an hour."

He did not answer; he glared at her.

Sighing, she patted his hand. "I do believe you. Yes, I

must! But simmer down, Benedict. Please do—and the Peter Boles affair will be forgotten."

Whether or not he was influenced by Hannah's gentle counsel, he did simmer down; and as she had predicted, the Peter Boles incident seemed soon to be forgotten. He mingled again with the townspeople and they were courteous to him. And if the *Fortune,* the *Sally* or the *Three Brothers* ever carried smuggled goods, no one was the wiser.

When winter came, he told Hannah that he was going to marry Margaret Mansfield, the daughter of New Haven's high sheriff. Margaret was three years younger than himself. She was demure and sweet, everything a man could wish for in a wife.

"I love her, and you will love her, too, Hannah," he said. "You'll live with us always. Not in this house. No, I'll build an elegant big house in Water Street. I know you're glad that I'm to be married."

Perhaps Hannah thought for a moment of a misty night in a long-ago summer, a shot in the darkness, a shy young Frenchman scared out of his wits—and out of her life forever. But she smiled warmly.

"I am glad, Benedict," she said. "I congratulate you. I hope you'll be very happy."

6

CLOUD ON THE HORIZON

BENEDICT ARNOLD AND MARGARET MANSFIELD WERE MARRIED February 22, 1767, and everyone said it was a very good match. The elegant big house in Water Street had not yet been built. Benedict took his bride to the modest but comfortable house which Hannah had kept for him.

A year later his first child was born, a son, who was named Benedict, according to the Arnold tradition; and in the summer of 1769, Richard, another son, was born. Both babies were sturdy and fine, a source of joy to their parents.

As for Hannah, she lavished all her affection upon these little nephews. They were her pets and treasures.

More than ever now, Benedict wanted to make money, a great lot of it, for himself and for his wife and children. His ships went more often to Canada and the West Indies. He cruised to many ports and became known everywhere as a sea captain, a shrewd trader, a vigorous tireless man with a hair-trigger temper.

A certain Captain Croskie had reason to remember Benedict Arnold's temper.

Croskie was an Englishman, the elderly master of a British ship. He liked to entertain and to play host to convivial comrades. Once, as his ship lay at anchor in the Bay of Honduras, Croskie sent cards to the officers of near-by British and American vessels, asking them to be his guests for the evening.

Benedict was in the cabin of the *Three Brothers* when a servant brought Captain Croskie's card to him. He sat at a desk stacked with ledgers, records and bills of lading. He had seldom been busier, for he would be sailing home the next week and there was much work to be done. The weather was stifling hot. Through an open porthole could be seen the green tropical shore line, steaming and shimmering in sunlight. Benedict was in his shirt sleeves, unkempt and sweating.

"What's this?" he said, glancing at the card. "I haven't even the time to answer it!"

He toiled at his papers until midnight, slept till dawn, then got up and dressed in his best clothes. Putting on his hat and gloves, he had two of his men row him to the British ship and went aboard.

"I'm inquiring for Captain Croskie," he said to a sailor on the deck. "I want to tell him why I could not attend last night's entertainment.

The sailor called Captain Croskie.

"Sir," Benedict said, "about last night—"

Captain Croskie looked at him disdainfully. "You damned Yankee! Have you no manners?"

Benedict's eyes narrowed, his jaw protruded. "My glove, sir." He drew the glove from his left hand and offered it.

"Your glove?" The British captain was incredulous. "You're not challenging me to a duel?"

"I am, sir," Benedict said, then bowed and descended to his rowboat.

Within the hour Williams, one of Captain Arnold's junior officers, was conferring with a junior officer of Captain Croskie's. They were to be seconds at the duel, which was scheduled for the next morning at five o'clock on a small island in the bay.

"Captain Croskie wishes to have his surgeon present," said the British junior officer.

Williams replied for Captain Arnold: "A surgeon, if you like. But no one else."

At the appointed hour, Benedict and Williams went to the island, but Croskie was not there; they waited.

At half-past five, Williams said, "I think he won't come, sir."

Benedict scowled. "Unless he's a cowering dog, he will come."

At six o'clock a long canoe was seen approaching. In it were Croskie, his junior officer, his surgeon and half a dozen West Indian natives. Benedict strode to the beach and leveled his pistol.

"Captain Croskie," he said, "you may come ashore with your second and your surgeon. The natives must pull away. Instantly!"

Captain Croskie rose, balancing himself unsteadily in the canoe. "Sir, the natives are all coming ashore—"

"If they do, I shall shoot them down, one by one."

The Englishmen then got out. The frightened natives pulled away.

The pistols were examined and checked. Croskie and Benedict walked to their places. As the challenged party to the duel, Croskie had the first shot. He fired, the bullet splintering bark from a tree. Benedict aimed deliberately at Croskie's left arm and fired. The bullet whistled and blood spurted from Croskie's arm, and the surgeon sprang forward to swathe it with clean linen.

Williams and the British junior officer reloaded. Croskie was pale as a ghost, his teeth clicking like dice in a box.

"I give you notice, sir," Benedict said, "that if you miss this time, I shall kill you."

Croskie lifted his gun, then hesitated. He turned to his second and muttered something.

"Captain Arnold," said the junior officer hastily, "Captain Croskie wishes to apologize to you."

"Ah? You mean he does not wish to be killed?" Benedict nodded. "He will state freely and voluntarily that I am a *gentleman?*"

"He will, sir."

"Very well." Benedict bowed ceremoniously. "Very well. I accept the apology.

In 1770 work was begun on Captain Arnold's house in Water Street. Benedict was determined that it should be as fine as any mansion in New Haven; therefore only the most expensive materials were used, the most skillful carpenters employed. Built of white clapboards, it had a portico and pillars, a marble fireplace in the parlor, a balustraded staircase and several large airy bedrooms. In an alcove just off the side door was a special cabinet in which Benedict would keep his shoes—he had shoes by the score, and all of them handsome. Beneath the kitchen was a wine cellar, from which a secret staircase wound upward to Benedict's library on the floor above.

The grounds were also fine. Enclosed by a white picket fence were several acres of lawn and gardens, with graveled paths to the stables and coach house. Adjoining the garden were Benedict's private wharves, and not far from the wharves was the new drugshop. From any of his windows, he could view Long Island Sound and the slim spars of his sailing vessels.

New Haven folk commented on the success of Benedict Arnold. Surely it was phenomenal! There he was, in his beautiful house, with such a charming family, his wife, his sister, two little sons—and now a third baby boy, who had been named Henry. He adored these children and was a model father to them. In turn he insisted that they must be good, and that they have proper instruction in virtue and goodness. From the cradle his sons must learn moral values, truth and honor.

Oh, occasionally it was hinted that Benedict Arnold might have some less admirable traits of character. Perhaps he was too rash, too sensitive. The clash with Captain Croskie? Yes, New Haven had heard of that, and of a more recent duel at Honduras—this one with a Captain Brookman, and with swords. Brookman, it was said, was severely injured, while Arnold emerged without a scratch.

But these tales might be exaggerated. They might even be falsehoods invented by people whose political opinions differed from Captain Arnold's.

For in Connecticut, and everywhere, there were undercurrents of strife now. Relations with England stretched thin; Americans were divided among themselves. Every American might soon have to decide whether to remain loyal to the King or to support those rebellious spirits who declared that the colonies should strike for independence and self-government.

And the Loyalists didn't all think alike. Some of them believed that King George ruled by divine right and must be obeyed without question. But a greater number were simply people who wished to avoid a crisis—war. Any kind of peace was to be preferred to war!

Events seemed to move steadily toward that crisis.

To oppose the Stamp Act men had banded together as the Sons of Liberty. The organization still existed, still cried out against taxation without representation, and the quartering of British soldiers in American towns and cities. In 1770 the Boston Massacre had occurred. Taunted by a mob of furious civilians, the red-coated British troopers had fired into the mob, killing three persons, mortally wounding two others. Later, there had been the Boston Tea Party—three hundred and forty-two chests of tea dumped into Boston Harbor by a little group of men disguised as Mohawk Indians who said that Americans would neither pay the tax nor let the tea ships dock.

To punish such arrogance, the king tightened his grip on the rebels, but they did not submit in silence. Quickly they had formed their Committees of Correspondence. North and south and back again, their indignant letters shuttled, weaving a web of communication. Now, in 1774, a Continental Congress held at Philadelphia united the colonies in a common purpose and effort.

What would the climax be? What *could* it be, but war?

Benedict Arnold did not dread war. At the time of the Boston Massacre he had said that Americans must take immediate vengeance on those murdering British soldiers! Freedom, he said, was a sacred thing, never to be renounced. The trouble brewing between the colonists and the mother country could never be smoothed out in a way satisfactory to all.

There were Loyalists living in New Haven.

"Tar and feather the Loyalists," Arnold recommended. "Ride them out of town on a rail!"

Additional companies of militia were being chartered in several of the colonies. In New Haven, sixty-five young men organized themselves as the Governor's Second Company of Guards. Each man provided his own weapons, his uniform of cockaded hat, scarlet coat faced with buff lapels, white waistcoat and breeches and black leggings. They elected Eleazar Oswald as one of their lieutenants and Benedict Arnold as their captain.

He was pleased and flattered and full of zeal. He read books on military tactics and studied maps of historic battlefields. He obtained a drummer, a fifer and a billowing silk banner of white and gold for the Guards, and he drilled them on the green.

His wife and Hannah and the little boys came to see the Guards parading. Everybody came to marvel at the resplendent sight; even on snowy days the green was lined with spectators.

Sometimes the men sang as they marched:

"Yankee doodle diddle doo,
Yankee doodle doo, sir,

The sober lads on Training Day,
Oh, they are mighty few, sir!"

And more often than not, the Guards finished their parade at Benedict's house, where they had a mug of tasty rum punch all around.

Friday, April 21, 1775, was a day to remember in New Haven. At noon, a horseman galloped into town with messages from Massachusetts. Two days earlier, April 19, at Lexington and Concord, there had been fighting—yes, actual fighting, bloodshed!—between British platoons and the colony's armed Minute Men.

The war, so long a cloud on the horizon, was now real and imminent.

7

TO ARMS!

THE CITIZENS OF NEW HAVEN WERE ALARMED BY THE NEWS from Massachusetts.

A war of rebellion? "No," said the Loyalists. "No!" And the more conservative patriots were not positive that they wanted to be drawn into it just yet; at a meeting that Friday afternoon, they voted against sending aid to the American forces mustering at Cambridge.

But Benedict Arnold was of another mind. It had always seemed to him that war was both inevitable—and right. Assembling his Guards, he addressed them in ringing tones.

"The British are in Boston," he said. "Who will march with me to defend our sacred liberties?"

Fifty of his men volunteered and several Yale College students begged to join the company. Delighted at the response, Arnold shook hands with them all.

"We go tomorrow morning," he said.

In the evening, he told his family and servants that this might be the onset of a long struggle for American independence, and that he would be in it to the end, fighting and sacrificing for the colonists' cause. While he was away, Hannah was to conduct his business, Margaret to look after the children. The servants must be faithful and shield the household from all harm.

Saturday morning he reassembled and inspected the Guards. A crowd was out to bid them farewell. The Reverend Jonathan Edwards, president of Yale, made a stirring speech in praise of these gallant young soldiers. Prayers were said for them.

And now they were ready to go—except for one thing. They had no ammunition for their shiny new guns.

Arnold knew that the town's selectmen were closeted together at the tavern, and that these officials had the keys to the powder house in which a quantity of ammunition was stored. He sent a sergeant to the tavern to get the keys. But the sergeant returned looking doleful.

"The selectmen wouldn't give them to me," the sergeant said.

Arnold was embarrassed. Why, the old grannies! He'd see about that!

He led his Guards to the tavern, halted them in the street and sent the sergeant in again.

"Tell the selectmen that if those keys aren't delivered within five minutes, I'll break down the powder house door and help myself," he said.

In less than five minutes, David Wooster came out from the meeting. Wooster was a man of sixty, a veteran of the French and Indian War, and the colonel of New Haven's older military company.

"Mr. Arnold," Wooster said, "the selectmen think you should delay your march—"

"Impossible, sir!"

"Will you not wait a day or two until you have orders—"

"From whom? No!" Arnold shouted. "None but Almighty God shall prevent my marching today!"

Colonel Wooster was Benedict Arnold's superior in rank; it was in his power to issue orders to the younger Guards. But he knew how savage Arnold could be when opposed and he wanted no outburst of temper here.

"Let me discuss it further with the selectmen," he said, and went into the tavern. Soon he was out once more. "The keys, sir." Sighing a little, he laid them on Arnold's extended palm.

Before noon the Guards were supplied with powder and ball from the powder house. Then, with their flag rippling overhead and to the tune of martial music, they stepped smartly off along the road.

Arnold was proud of them; and at Wethersfield, where they were greeted with cheers and huzzas, he read aloud a document he had prepared for them. The document pledged them to obey their officers in everything, and forbade drunkenness, gambling or profanity.

"I want you men to sign the pledge," Arnold said.

They did so, and he affixed his own flourishing signature.

Halfway between Hartford and Cambridge, Arnold was hailed by an old acquaintance Colonel Samuel H. Parsons, who was hastening back to Connecticut to recruit for the Colonial Army. Parsons had some late reports for Arnold: More than four thousand soldiers had rallied to the rebellion, the Massachusetts Committee of Safety was organizing them into units.

"But we have so few cannons," Parsons said. "It's our weakness—and what's to be done about it?"

Arnold had thought of that. "As you know," he said, "my business has often taken me northward into the lake region. At Fort Ticonderoga good brass cannons are rusting for lack of use—and the fort is held by a small detachment of British troops. My notion would be to move on Ticonderoga, capture the cannons and establish a base near the Canadian border."

Colonel Parsons considered this. "Have you presented your notion anywhere?"

"Not yet, but I will."

"Well, sir, it is a time of stress," Parsons said.

Arnold saluted. "It is, but our cause is glorious!"

Cambridge was thronged with recruits, most of them untrained and poorly officered. By contrast, Arnold's men were trim and disciplined. He marched them to the house of the Massachusetts governor, which was empty—for the Governor was a Loyalist and had fled from the town. Without consulting the Cambridge officials, Arnold installed his Guards in the big rambling mansion. It would be their quarters, he said, and his right to it was not disputed. Indeed, everyone acknowledged that these newcomers surpassed all the other American units in appearance and bearing; and as their captain, Arnold was much complimented.

But he was eager for action, and he hadn't forgotten his talk with Colonel Parsons. Very soon he presented to the Committee of Safety his plan for the conquest of Fort Ticonderoga. The committee listened and approved. Arnold was commissioned as a colonel in the Continental Army, granted money, ammunition and horses, told to raise a force of four hundred men in Western Massachusetts and to proceed with his expedition.

Smiling and excited, he left his Guards in Cambridge and galloped west to recruit. At Stockbridge, he received the dismaying news that Ethan Allen of Vermont had just started out on the same mission.

Ethan Allen!

Arnold had heard of Ethan Allen, a huge, strapping, blustering fellow who had been involved in a kind of border warfare with the colonial government of New York. Allen was almost an outlaw; he headed a band of swaggering comrades known as the Green Mountain Boys. It was said of Allen that he was so tough he could bite a tenpenny nail in two: his Boys were no better than brigands.

The American officer who could seize Fort Ticonderoga from the British would be a hero. And was Ethan Allen to have this honor?

"Never!" Arnold vowed. "Never!"

The people of Stockbridge told Arnold that Ethan Allen had with him a batch of volunteers from Hartford.

"But has he a *commission?*" Arnold asked.

The Stockbridge people didn't know. Allen had been somewhat vague about a commission.

Well, Benedict was not vague about his commission. It was penned with black ink on white paper, folded into a pocket of his colorful coat. But how foolish he had been to speak so frankly to Colonel Parsons—for surely Parsons was to blame for the mix-up!

Cursing Parsons as a meddler, and especially cursing Ethan Allen, Arnold sprang to his horse and galloped frantically toward Lake Champlain.

Before dawn, he caught up with the swashbuckling Vermonter. It was May 10; Allen was at Hand's Cove on the lake shore, loading his men into boats, intending to cross under cover of darkness for a surprise attack on the fort. Vaulting from the saddle, Arnold hurried to stop him.

"This is my expedition," he said, and produced his commission. "My expedition, and I shall command it."

Ethan Allen squinted at the paper and rubbed his stubbled chin.

"No," he said. "No, I reckon not, Mr. Arnold."

"*Colonel* Arnold! The idea was mine. I thought of it."

"I've been thinking of those Ticonderoga cannons myself," Allen said. "So have John Brown and James Easton of Connecticut, two men in my party. But, as you can plainly see, sir, I'm in charge; and it's just your bad luck to be a mite tardy this morning."

Arnold was incensed. "You will give place to me, sir!"

"Stand off now, Colonel Arnold," Allen said. "I've got to put my boys over the lake and it'll soon be daylight. No time to dawdle."

Arnold did not stand off. "I shall assume command!"

Allen appealed to the Green Mountain Boys. "What'll I do with the rascal?"

"Oh, let him go with us," somebody said.

But a howl arose. The Green Mountain Boys would not have this dandified little rooster directing them; they'd turn tail and go home, first. And the volunteers from Hartford declared that Ethan Allen was their leader, no one else.

Allen grinned. "Colonel Arnold, it seems to me more important to get going than to chew the rag about who's boss.

Tell you what, we'll play we're partners. You come along in the boat with me—but I'll give the orders."

Arnold clambered into the boat, for light was streaking the sky and he could think of nothing more to do or say. The oarsmen pulled with might and main; the other boats followed and beached at a rocky ledge north of the fort. Arnold counted the men; there were eighty-five of them. Quietly they edged toward a wicket gate in the stone wall. A drowsy sentry was at the gate. They sprang at the sentry, gagged him and slipped into the fort's enclosure.

Ethan Allen had a voice like thunder and now he roared the order to attack. All shouting, the men swarmed in upon the barracks where forty-two British soldiers were sleeping.

A white-faced young lieutenant showed himself at the barracks door.

"By—by what authority are you here?" he quavered.

"In the name of the great Jehovah and the Continental Congress," Allen thundered.

The lieutenant ran to summon his captain, while the Green Mountain Boys rioted and yelled raucously around the parade ground, in and out of the crumbling buildings. Dragged from bed, the British captain knew at once that resistance would be futile. With scarcely a word, he surrendered his sword and the fort.

But he surrendered them to Ethan Allen—not to Benedict Arnold.

Though Arnold had doggedly kept abreast of the rugged, iron-lunged backwoodsman as they entered the fort, he might as well have remained at Hand's Cove, for all the attention paid him. He, too, had barked out orders; they were drowned in the din. When Allen denounced the British officers as "skunks" and threatened to skin them alive, Arnold had said that the rules of war must be remembered—no slaughter, no plundering!—but he was not heeded.

The Green Mountain Boys tore through the fort, despoiling it. Kegs of liquor were in the cellar; they opened the kegs and got very drunk. Some of the buildings in the enclosure housed the families of the married soldiers. The Boys ransacked these buildings, stole everything of value, dressed up in the women's cloaks and bonnets and amused themselves by tormenting the terrified children.

Completely ignored, Arnold could only look on helplessly. A drunken mountaineer poked a rifle at his chest.

"You're not the commander here! You're not even the commander's partner. Admit it, or I'll blow you to smithereens!"

Unflinchingly Arnold stared at the man until he dropped his gun and shambled away.

Ethan Allen had visited the cellar. Red with rum, he accosted Arnold.

"Leave the fort!" he roared. "Leave it!"

"I have a duty to the colony of Massachusetts," Arnold replied coldly. "I shall stay—and insist upon my rights."

That night he wrote a report to the Committee of Safety in Cambridge. Ethan Allen and his friends were still roistering. Arnold had never felt more lonely or sick at heart. He wondered whether, after all, the victory at Ticonderoga was as important as this crushing disappointment to his ambitions.

He told the committee that Ethan Allen might be the proper person to lead these wild people who seemed to worship him, but that he was totally devoid of military ability. Ticonderoga, he said, had yielded up a vast amount of guns and other armaments; he would endeavor to send these stores back to Cambridge.

"I am extremely sorry that matters have not been transacted with more prudence and judgment," he wrote, and added that he had done everything he could. "I hope soon to be released from this troublesome business."

8

ON LAKE CHAMPLAIN

FOR THE NEXT THREE DAYS ARNOLD WAS UTTERLY MISERABLE, for the Green Mountain Boys continually badgered him. Twice he was shot at by the drunken revelers, and always they mocked and ridiculed him.

"So you're commanding Ticonderoga?" they said. "And where are your troops, General Arnold?"

Alas, he had no troops—and no one to talk to except the captured British officers who, though enemies, were educated gentlemen at least.

James Easton was going back to Cambridge; he said he would take with him Arnold's report to the Massachusetts Committee of Safety. Easton was one of Ethan Allen's men. Arnold did not like him, but he couldn't go himself to Cambridge and he wanted the committee to know the truth about his situation. Rather reluctantly, he gave the papers to Easton. Afterward, and too late, he realized that Easton would probably trick him.

But on the fourth day, suddenly he felt much better. A two-masted schooner loomed on the lake and landed below the fort. Eleazar Oswald and fifty men were aboard—Arnold's men, recruited by Eleazar in Massachusetts. The schooner had belonged to a Loyalist named Philip Skene.

"We grabbed it," Eleazar said, wringing Arnold's hand. "Nice, isn't it? Can you use it?"

Yes, Arnold could use the ship, for he had been thinking of something.

"I've had plenty of leisure for thinking, Eleazar! There's a large British sloop anchored above the lake in the Sorel

River, just off the town of St. Johns. We'll sail north and get that sloop. Then we'll control Champlain from top to bottom."

Eleazar smiled jauntily. "When do we start?"

"As soon as we can arm the schooner!"

As they worked, transferring some of Ticonderoga's big guns to the schooner, Arnold told Eleazar of another wonderful plan he had brooded over in these days of vexation and solitude.

"The war must be carried into Canada," he said. "If the British decide to invade the colonies, it will be by way of Canada, down the chain of lakes and rivers—we must block the passage! And most of the Canadians are French. They were conquered by the British in the last war, and they've never learned to love their conquerors. I think they might rally to us, might even become a fourteenth American colony."

Eleazar looked admiringly at his friend. "It's a bold plan, Benedict. On the grand scale."

"It's practical," Arnold said.

By nightfall the schooner was in readiness, and Arnold had obtained two bateaux, lightweight river boats, which would be towed behind. He was happy, almost gay, for here was an expedition that Ethan Allen couldn't lead! Allen was not a sailor, but Benedict Arnold's experiences at sea had trained him for just such a project.

Early next morning the schooner glided rapidly north. Two days later it was nearing St. Johns and sailing less rapidly because of a slackening wind.

As evening came on, Arnold ordered an anchorage.

"We'll take to the bateaux," he said.

Thirty-five men boarded the bateaux and rowed all night. At dawn they were out of the boats, creeping up the riverbank. At six o'clock, they pounced on the town, seizing not only the sloop, but also a small company of British soldiers and nine more bateaux. Then with their prizes they sped to the schooner. The wind had freshened and they sailed south again.

"And none too soon!" Eleazar exclaimed, glancing back at the St. Johns waterfront. "The British reinforcements are gathering. Well, it was a brilliant stroke, brilliantly managed, Benedict."

"And what will Allen say?"

Eleazar laughed. "You're a strange fellow, aren't you? I believe that outwitting Allen pleases you more than getting the sloop."

"Maybe not more," Arnold said, "but as much."

At noon the men on the schooner were astonished to see several little boats approaching from the south. Ethan Allen and his mountaineers were crammed into the boats. Arnold saluted them with a cannon blast, and Allen fired his musket in response.

"Where are you bound for?" Arnold called.

"St. Johns," Allen roared. "To occupy the town."

Arnold waved them on. "They'll be chased out like rats," he said gleefully. "And good enough for them!"

With the sloop and men to do his bidding, Arnold set about transporting the cannons from Ticonderoga to the southern tip of Lake George, where they could be picked up and hauled overland to Cambridge. He inspected and repaired the fort that the British had abandoned at Crown Point. His schooner patrolled Lake Champlain. He wrote a report of his labors; and to make sure that this one would be received, he sent it by his own courier.

As he had expected, Ethan Allen could not hold St. Johns. In a week Allen was back at Ticonderoga, but still boastful. Hating him, Arnold moved up to the Crown Point fort. Many of the Green Mountain Boys were becoming bored now and wandering home to their hilly farms. It seemed to Arnold—and perhaps to Allen, too—that in the rivalry between them, Arnold would soon be the winner.

But then a series of disturbing things happened. Word came that the Continental Congress wanted the Americans to withdraw entirely from the lake district.

"Withdraw? We can't. We won't!" Arnold said. "I shall write and tell the congressmen so."

He had scarcely dispatched his protest to Congress when James Easton returned from Cambridge. If Arnold had not liked Easton before, now he detested him. He suspected that Easton had not delivered his report to the Committee of Safety. They began to quarrel. Arnold sprang at Easton, smashed his fist into his face and knocked him down.

Easton had a cutlass and a brace of pistols in his belt.

"Get up!" Arnold cried. "Get up and fight!"

Easton did not get up, but lay there moaning. Arnold jerked him to his feet, kicked him and ordered him to be off.

Ethan Allen and some of his men had seen this exhibition of Arnold's temper. Eleazar Oswald had seen it, too, and he was worried.

"Allen will tell everybody, Benedict," Eleazar said. "You may be sure that the story will be passed around, and probably exaggerated. You'll be hurt by it."

"I don't care," Arnold asserted. "Allen is doing everything possible to displace me, anyway. Allen is a numskull, Easton a liar, and I don't fear either of them."

As his anger cooled, he wrote another letter to Congress, outlining his plan for a campaign in Canada, even to details. He said that if no one else would undertake the campaign, he himself would do so—and "with the smiles of Heaven," he would succeed. Of course, he must have adequate supplies and troops.

"And no Green Mountain Boys," he added emphatically.

The letter was too important to be entrusted to any ordinary courier. He sent Eleazar to Philadelphia with it. He felt that his plan had not a single flaw. It was perfect; he was confident that it would be accepted.

But the war was still very new to the American colonies, and there was a great deal of confusion in Congress. The conflicting reports from the north only increased the tangle. Benedict Arnold claimed to be the commander at Ticonderoga. Ethan Allen made the same claim.

Which one was to be believed?

In June, a third commander arrived on Lake Champlain. He was Colonel Benjamin Hinman; he had a thousand militiamen with him. Hinman met Arnold at Crown Point and said he had been commissioned to relieve him.

"Relieve me?" Arnold said haughtily. "Where are your orders, sir?"

"The Connecticut government body sent me," Hinman replied. "I have as yet no regular orders."

"Then I will not turn over the post to you," Arnold said.

Hinman was young and somewhat in awe of this glowering older officer. He took his men to Ticonderoga, where they quietly encamped.

A few days later Arnold had more visitors. A committee of three Massachusetts legislators appeared at Crown Point. They had come to investigate the northern command—and particularly, Colonel Arnold's behavior. The committee decided that Colonel Hinman was the rightful commander. Colonel Arnold could be Hinman's second in command.

"I will not be second to any person whomsoever!" Arnold announced. "Never, sirs! If that is your judgment, I shall resign from the army!"

The next day he resigned. Dismissing the men Eleazar had brought to him on the schooner, he started southward.

He was not well; many weeks had passed since he had heard from his family and he felt depressed and unappreciated. As he went on, he thought bitterly of the insults he had endured—and of the money he had spent out of his own pocket to repair the sloop, the old buildings at Ticonderoga and Crown Point. It was money he needed for Margaret and the children, money he might never recover.

He stopped at Albany and here he learned why no recent letters from Margaret had come to him. Margaret was dead. A month ago, his dear wife had died of the fever.

Sorrowfully he went on to New Haven and trudged into his fine house, to weep with Hannah and his three little sons.

"Hannah," he said, "I've lost everything. What am I to do now?"

As always Hannah consoled him.

"You have a duty to your country; you haven't lost that," she said. "Go back to the army, Benedict. Let me keep the children. I'll try to be a mother to them."

9

THROUGH THE WILDERNESS

ON THE LAST DAY OF JULY ARNOLD RODE TO CAMBRIDGE TO make his formal report to the Massachusetts Committee of Safety. He was still not well. Hannah watched him anxiously as he mounted his horse.

"I'll not be gone long, Hannah," he said.

"Perhaps you will, though," she said. "Yes, I've the presentiment that you will. But don't be uneasy. I'll see to the shop and the wharves. And the little lads, too."

He was touched. "You're a good sister to stand by me so stanchly."

"And what's a sister for, if not to stand by?" she retorted.

In Cambridge he had a tedious session with the committee. He was asked how he had spent the money granted to him in April. He explained; the committee seemed to think he had been extravagant. He spoke of the sum he himself had advanced, and was told that only a fraction of it could be repaid now, the balance must be collected later.

Nothing was said about his dashing and profitable raid on St. Johns. He guessed that somebody—either James Easton or Ethan Allen, or both—had prejudiced the committee against him, and he felt abused and mistreated.

But in spite of all this, he was interested to see Cambridge again. The town was full of soldiers, for the British were occupying Boston, and around that city on every side, blockading and besieging it, were regiments of Americans. A battle had been fought at Bunker Hill, a battle won by the British, but at a tremendous cost to them in killed and wounded.

The colonies now had fourteen thousand men in arms, and George Washington of Virginia had been made their commander in chief. Washington was wise and fair; no man in America was more beloved and respected. On July 3, at Cambridge, Washington had assumed his command; and now Arnold had the opportunity to talk with him.

Washington had read Arnold's letter containing the plan for a Canadian campaign—and other similar plans submitted by other people. He said he had decided to send General Philip Schuyler of New York up from Lake Champlain to attack Montreal, and wanted a second force to go north through the Maine wilderness to attack Quebec.

A two-pronged drive on Canada, he said. Wasn't this what Colonel Arnold had proposed? And would Arnold lead the march to Quebec?

"Yes, your Excellency," Arnold answered instantly.

"It is a difficult task, Colonel Arnold."

"I do not shrink from it, sir."

In fact, he was most grateful. This would be his chance—the chance to prove his strength and skill! Perhaps in the wilderness he could forget the slights and injustices he had smarted under at Ticonderoga. In performing a difficult task, his grief for Margaret would be soothed.

They discussed the campaign. It should begin before bad weather set in, Arnold said. He knew how terrible the Canadian winters were. He mapped the route he would follow. It was one marked out by missionaries and hunters a century ago: by boat up the Kennebec River, into the Maine mountains, then through small lakes to the sluggish Dead River, over a plateau known as the Height of Land, from there through a river so swift and turbulent that it seemed to boil, and was called by the French the Chaudiere, or Cauldron.

"The Chaudiere empties into the St. Lawrence at a point just across from Quebec," he said—and already he imagined himself on the St. Lawrence shore, gazing at the steep walls of Quebec.

Washington nodded gravely. "The Continental Congress

has been endeavoring to persuade the people of southern Canada to join our rebellion. But they are timid and they have no troops. If we could get possession of Montreal and Quebec, their attitude might change. General Schuyler is at Ticonderoga now. I shall urge him to start for Montreal. And you, Colonel Arnold, can be making your preparations."

As he shook Washington's hand in parting, Arnold was exultant. Whether or not Schuyler took Montreal, he—Benedict Arnold—would take Quebec! Thus far, only one man in the world had ever done so: James Wolfe, the British general who in the French and Indian War had captured Canada's great rocky fortress for his king. The name of James Wolfe, the fame of his exploit, would live forever in military history.

"And mine, too," Arnold said to himself. *"My name, my fame."*

His first job was to recruit an army, and in this he was fortunate. Many New England soldiers, sweltering in summer heat, thought yearningly of the cool breezes in Canada. He got together a thousand of them, including some capable officers. From Virginia came a company of rangy frontiersmen, wearing hunting shirts and moccasins, armed with rifles, tomahawks and scalping knives. Daniel Morgan, a veteran Indian fighter, was their captain.

"Arnold's shirttail men with the cursed, twisted guns," the New Englanders called these sinewy troopers who walked as silently as cats and whose aim was so cunning.

"And I am glad to have them," Arnold said. "I need them."

But there were some annoyances connected with the recruiting period. The Continental Congress was sometimes balky. He had asked that Eleazar Oswald be made a lieutenant; the request was denied.

"I'll go as a volunteer, then," Eleazar said sensibly.

"A volunteer—and my secretary. I insist upon that, and

it's little enough," Arnold said. "I've somehow offended Congress—and you're suffering the consequences."

Eleazar smiled. "Oh, don't fret about it. I won't. Who am I, really? Only one of a thousand fellows eager to serve the cause, not entitled to any special consideration. I don't care how I serve; I've never cared. Just so I serve."

Arnold regarded his friend curiously. "Is that the way you feel?"

"Yes, certainly." Eleazar's eyes twinkled. "Don't you?"

"Perhaps," Arnold said. "Or perhaps I'm more ambitious."

From a shipbuilder in Maine he ordered two hundred bateaux, each boat to accommodate six or seven men, their luggage and gear.

"And hurry," he told the shipbuilder. "Hurry!"

Next he purchased barrels and crates of food and ammunition. And then he waited for word that General Schuyler had left Ticonderoga for Montreal.

He waited for weeks while the summer days slipped by. What detained Schuyler? Inquiring of Washington, he heard that Schuyler was ill, General Richard Montgomery would command Schuyler's regiments, that Montgomery was now marshaling his men.

"I'm always waiting for something, somebody," Arnold said to Oswald. "This waiting could be disastrous. If the scheme is postponed much longer, it will be worthless. I think I'll give it up."

Oswald protested. "No, you can't. Be patient."

Washington and his adjutant General Horatio Gates also counseled patience.

"Patience, Colonel Arnold."

At last he was allowed to start. On September 16 his army congregated at Newburyport, Massachusetts, and embarked in a fleet of fishing vessels for the mouth of the Kennebec, where the new bateaux were moored.

They were not good bateaux; he saw it at a glance. Smaller

than specified, they had been made too hastily of green wood. Canoes, he thought, might have been better. But he hadn't the time to go looking for canoes. He ordered twenty more of the bateaux and told Eleazar to get him one canoe.

"I'll have to keep ahead to chart our course," he said.

He talked with some woodsmen who had just recently come from Canada. British troopers and spies infested the forest around the Chaudiere River, the woodsmen said; and Sir Guy Carleton, the king's governor of Canada, was expecting an American invasion.

"And beware of the Indian chief Natanis," the woodsmen warned. "Natanis is a spy for Carleton."

Arnold felt that the weather was more of a danger than were a few scattered Britishers and their Indian spies. He sent out his own scouts, then launched his boats up the Kennebec. Oswald had found a slim, speedy canoe for him and two Indian guides to paddle it. He took his place at the end of the line, but soon the canoe had passed the slower bateaux and he was leading.

He was in high spirits; the sun shone, the men were cheerful. Most of them operated the boats, but some marched along the riverbank to help the bateaux through the narrower channels, or to cut paths in spots where the supplies must be carried. It was no uncommon thing for a bateau to be stranded in the shallows, or upset as it scraped on hidden reefs. Such mishaps seemed to amuse the men. They laughed to see their companions flung into the water, wading in mud. Everybody was good-natured. This was like a camping trip, the men said. Arduous, yes, but exciting and pleasant.

When they were through the Kennebec, Arnold halted in the shadow of the mountains to talk with his scouts.

"What about the Indians?"

The scouts had seen none.

"This big chief Natanis?"

No, the scouts said, the northern country seemed all quiet.

He inspected his boats; many of them were leaking. He counted his barrels and crates; much of the flour supply had spoiled and hundreds of loaves of bread were moldy and would have to be dumped as trash.

"Short rations," he said to his officers. "Unless we hurry, food may be a problem."

Now they turned toward the lakes and the plateau, where the bateaux must be pulled or dragged from one lake to the next. The ground was spongy and moist, with frequent swamps and quagmires. Progress was slow; the men toiled and sweated.

When they came to the Dead River, Arnold sent messages to Washington.

"We have been a month in the wilderness," he wrote. "This river is deep and gentle. We are nearing the Canadian border."

It rained that day and all through the night, hard and drenching. The next day there was more rain, a cloudburst of rain, and a wind as fierce and blustering as a hurricane. The river which had looked so gentle began to swell. By evening it was twice its normal size.

Cold, tired and very wet, the men wrapped themselves in their blankets to sleep. At four o'clock in the morning they were awakened by crashing noises as immense dams of driftwood and fallen trees rushed downstream, washing over the boats, sinking seven of them, snatching away precious baggage and provisions.

At dawn, Arnold climbed to a hilltop to survey the flood. Though the sun shone again, water strewn with wreckage surged and swirled everywhere, lashed by a whistling wind.

He conferred with his officers.

"Well, shall we go on?" he asked.

The officers were thoughtful. There was considerable sickness among the men. The temperature had dropped, ice crusted the shallows. Soaked clothing was freezing rigid and campfires could not be kindled. And the prospect they faced was even more dismal—unknown territory that might be spiked with guns.

With food so scarce, they might also face starvation.

But the officers were not unwilling; they believed the men were not unwilling.

"I can get food," Arnold said resolutely. "I've studied my maps. We're in the neighborhood of some French villages on the Chaudiere. I'll lead a rescue party to buy food from the French."

The rescue party left at noon—Arnold in the canoe, with Eleazar Oswald and fifty picked riflemen following in four of the bateaux. During their absence the rest of the men were to proceed as best they could over the Height of Land and into Canada. Arnold ordered that the other bateaux be discarded; they were too battered to be of any use.

"And besides," he said ruefully, "nothing remains to be packed in them.

Snow was falling as the canoe swerved into the current and was caught up by the flood. Sweeping around bends and through rapids, the bateaux were not far behind, a man with a pole standing in the bow of each one to fend off boulders, while in the sterns the steering oars churned the frothing waves. The pace was fast, then faster.

After fifteen miles Arnold heard a thud, shouts, splashings. Looking back, he saw that two of the bateaux had splintered to pieces on a mass of jutting stone and a third boat had capsized. The water's surface was dotted with men who swam desperately for the shore—knowing that they must swim or be drowned, for they couldn't be picked up. Somehow, and on foot, they would have to return to the marching column on the Height of Land.

The canoe and the fourth bateau went onward, lurching and winding into the even more tumultuous Chaudiere. There were two days of this mad race. On the third day Arnold noticed that the river had widened; it flowed between banks where patches of meadow interspersed the forest.

Cultivated fields slid into view. At evening smoke could be seen against the sky, then a cluster of Indian wigwams, houses and barns, grazing cattle—people!

Leaping from the canoe, he waded to the beach.

"Food!" he shouted. "Beef! Bread!"

He had money for the French villagers, and they were not unfriendly. He bought a whole herd of cattle and sacks of other supplies which could be borne on their backs to the Height of Land.

Two days later the rescue party came within sight of the marchers. And what a pitiful sight it was! Laboring uphill to the plateau, the men had floundered in snow and ice, gone astray, wandered into pits and bogs. Dozens of them had died of exposure; those who lived were like walking skeletons. Frantic with hunger, they had gnawed on their moccasins and belts. They had cooked and eaten a pet dog. They had drunk broth made of their leather shot pouches, buckskin breeches and shaving soap. Gaunt, half clad, in a slow straggling line they had plodded forward as if dazed.

But now Colonel Arnold was here—with food! He had saved them. Laughing and crying, they feebly blessed him.

At dusk they saw a band of Indians creeping toward them. It was the chief Natanis and eighty of his tribesmen, painted and feathered, adorned with beads, bracelets and scalp locks.

Arnold halted; the Indians came closer.

"You do not fear me, Colonel Arnold?" Natanis said.

"I fear nothing," Arnold answered.

"We have trailed you for many weeks." Natanis smiled slyly. "We have been ever at your heels, and you did not dream of it."

"Why have you trailed me?"

"To discover what manner of man you are. Now we know that you are brave, you are the Dark Eagle." Natanis lifted his bare brown hand and gestured mysteriously. "The Dark

Eagle comes to claim the wilderness. The wilderness will yield to the Dark Eagle, but the Rock will defy him. The Dark Eagle will soar aloft to the sun. Nations will behold him and sound his praises. Yet when he soars highest his fall is most certain. When his wings brush the sky, then the arrow will pierce his heart."

Arnold frowned. Was this a prophecy?

"I am not superstitious, Natanis," he said. "Do our brethren, the Indians, desire to fight with us against the English oppressors?"

Natanis looked around at his tribesmen; they were murmuring and nodding.

"Yes," Natanis said, "we will fight with you, Dark Eagle."

Arnold had sailed up the Kennebec with a thousand soldiers. On November 8, he reached the St. Lawrence with six hundred, a bearded, scarecrow throng dressed in rags and tatters.

Light snow frosted the ground; a chill, penetrating gale blew from the north. On the far shore, poised on granite bluffs, were the fortifications of Quebec. Below these sheer walls, strung along the river were streets of houses, warehouses and docks. Patrolling the river were British guard boats, a frigate of twenty-six guns and a sloop.

"Quebec is actually two towns," Arnold said to Eleazar Oswald. "The one above, which is the fort, the citadel, and its defenses, and the Lower Town at the water's edge. We'll have to cross to the Lower Town, then ascend and take the citadel."

Eleazar shivered, his teeth chattering. "We can't cross today. Not in this fiendish wind."

"Oh, no, it must be done at night. We'll wait for a lull." He sighed. "More waiting!"

"But cross in *what?*" Eleazar asked.

"Boats, canoes. That's why I wanted Natanis," Arnold said. "To get boats for us."

10

THE BATTLE FOR QUEBEC

AS HE WAITED ON THE WEATHER, SCOUTS BROUGHT INFORMATION from Quebec. The citadel had been recently reinforced, the scouts said, with troops, guns and powerful cannons. Spies had told the British officers that an American army might come, and the occupants of the fort were bracing for a battle.

"Of course, we're being spied on right now," Arnold said to Oswald. "And how do I know that some of my own men are not betraying us?"

Spies, traitors, deserters—he hated them all.

He learned also that General Montgomery was in Canada and at any moment might attack Montreal. And he received one bit of information that made him smile: Ethan Allen, with a little company of recruits like his Green Mountain Boys—but without authority—had tried to capture Montreal. Instead, Allen had been captured. As a prisoner of war, Ethan Allen would be shipped to England.

The Indians had found birchbark canoes and flat-bottomed dories for Arnold. The night of November 13 was cold, cloudy, but calm; and he decided to risk a crossing of the St. Lawrence.

He got five hundred of his men into the boats; quietly they paddled to midstream, drifted past the British patrol and landed. Ten canoes started back for the rest of the men. But suddenly the moon shone out from behind clouds, and from one of the British barges a voice rose querulously.

"Who goes there?"

"Hist!" Arnold murmured. "The others will have to follow when they can."

He led the five hundred to the outskirts of the Lower Town. A dim shape appeared at his elbow. It was Natanis to say that the path to the fortifications above was clear. On the ramparts, a British sentry was calling, "All's well!"

Treading softly, the Americans climbed the steep, stony path to the broad level called the Plains of Abraham. They halted and saw the fort before them. Big and black it loomed, the gates shut, the walls too high and sheer to be scaled without ladders. In the last hours of darkness Arnold marshaled his men into battle formation—and there, at daybreak, they were seen by the British sentries.

Arnold was ready; he thought he would be fired on. But the British did not fire. Soldiers and civilians from inside the fort crowded to the parapets and stared down at these wild-looking strangers.

Then Arnold paraded his men. Yowling like panthers, the Americans dared the British to come out—"Come out, you redcoats! Show yourselves!"

Nothing happened.

Arnold sent an envoy to one of the gates, a soldier with a white flag of truce and the demand for surrender. The envoy was shot at, escaping death by a hair's breadth. This was contrary to every rule of civilized warfare, and Arnold was wrathful. But he told his men to hold their fire. What would be the good of lambasting stone walls?

"We haven't much ammunition," he said. "We can't afford to waste it."

A panting messenger arrived on the Plains with a note for Arnold from General Montgomery. Montreal had been taken, but Sir Guy Carleton, the king's governor of Canada and commander of the royal troops, had wriggled out of Montgomery's net. Carleton was now on his way to Quebec, with the remnants of his regiment, and Montgomery would soon come to Arnold's assistance.

So there would be no battle here today? No, because how could you have a battle with enemies who would neither show themselves nor surrender? Angrily, Arnold marched his men to Pointe aux Trembles, twenty miles west on the river. He would have to wait again, for more powder and ball, for ladders—for Montgomery. His determination to conquer Quebec was not one whit diminished. He would do it! But to have to share the victory seemed unfair. He felt displeased and cheated.

Montgomery came down the St. Lawrence on a schooner December 3, bringing with him three hundred troopers, bales of clothing, several cannons and ammunition. He was a slender, intelligent-looking young man. English born, he had been a captain in the British army; but his sympathy was with the colonists and in the early days of the rebellion he had offered them his services.

Arnold had thought he would dislike Montgomery, for he resented his superior rank. But as they talked he realized Montgomery wanted to be his friend.

"Your corps is exceedingly fine, Colonel Arnold," Montgomery said. "It has splendid style and discipline."

Later Arnold said to Eleazar Oswald: "We'll get on together, I think, Montgomery and I."

Eleazar glanced up from a ledger in which he was jotting figures. "Well, why shouldn't you? Benedict, if your scouts are correct, there are eighteen hundred Britishers inside the citadel. With Montgomery's men and Natanis' Indians we have a combined force of less than a thousand. Hmm!"

"It's enough for the job," Arnold said.

It began to snow that day and for ten days it snowed steadily. Through knee-deep snow the combined forces tramped back to the Plains of Abraham, sought shelter in near-by barns, cowsheds and vacant farmhouses, constructed entrenchments of ice blocks to screen the cannons. In the city of Quebec the snow piled up to the second floor windows of houses and lay in great white ridges against the outer walls of the fort.

Occasionally a gun crackled and boomed, as the Americans and the British exchanged shots. Occasionally the enemies yelled impudent threats.

"We've got you bottled up, you redcoat lobsters! Bottled and sealed!"

"Ah, what odds, Yankees? What odds?"

The odds were that the Americans were running short of food; they were very cold, some of them sick with smallpox. This worried Arnold. Healthy himself, he never minded privations of any kind, but he knew his men were thinking of their warm homes and loving families in New England.

"Most of them enlisted in the summer for six months," he told General Montgomery. "In January they can go home if they want to; I can't prevent it. We must take Quebec soon."

"Now or never?" Montgomery looked at the falling snow. "Yes, I agree. We have scaling ladders now, and some artillery. I suggest a nighttime attack, with the snow making a curtain to hide our movements."

"A good suggestion," Arnold said. "You can approach the Lower Town from the southwest, I'll march from the northeast. At a central point, we'll unite and advance upon those inclined paths to the fort."

Montgomery nodded. "Tomorrow night, Colonel Arnold."

But the next morning was bright and sunny. Just when the curtain of thick white flakes was needed, it vanished. For two weeks there was no snowfall.

At last, on December 30, a blizzard blew in, with snow and sleet.

Arnold summoned his men at midnight. They descended from the Plains and filed from a northeasterly direction into the streets of the Lower Town—Arnold leading, then artillerymen pulling a sled on which a cannon was strapped, then Captain Daniel Morgan with the sharpshooters, then the other soldiers, company by company.

The blizzard was terrible, blinding. They had to walk

with bent heads, clutching their guns beneath their coats so that the powder and locks should not be dampened. On each man's cap was pinned a piece of paper, for purposes of identification, if the groups became separated. Scribbled on each paper were the words—*Liberty or Death.*

The streets were crooked and walled, but Arnold knew of openings in them. He went through a portal called the Palace Gate; a scout emerged from a doorway to whisper that Montgomery's column was marching in along the river road.

Abruptly a rocket arched upward, flared and winked out. It was Montgomery's signal for the assault on the Lower Town.

Arnold unsheathed his sword, shouted and began to run forward.

Instantly church bells clanged, all the church bells in Quebec clanging in unison. Lights glimmered in the fort above. The guns of the British sentries sounded an alarm.

Arnold sprinted through a street of shops. He heard a roar of muskets behind him—his men had been fired on and were returning the fire. The street narrowed; there were black-dark houses on both sides. He knew that a barrier stood at the end of this street; he intended to demolish the barrier with his cannon. He paused, wanting to see the barrier smashed. What he saw was the empty sled. The artillerymen had plunged into a snowdrift; the cannon was buried under tons of snow.

He gave the order to advance, anyway, ordering the men to batter down the wooden barrier with their gunstocks. But now the windows in these dark houses creaked open, from every one the snouts of rifles poked out, raking the street with a sheet of fire. Somewhere in front of him a cannon exploded with a noise that made the earth quiver like jelly. A score of his men were mowed down. Rifles rattled hideously and he felt a pain in his left leg. He staggered and sprawled in the snow.

He got up, stumbled a step or two, but he knew he could not walk. Leaning against a wall, he shouted to Captain Morgan, to all those who hammered and pounded at the barrier: "Rush on, brave boys! *Rush on!*

He saw Morgan push through to the street beyond.

They'll seize the fort, he thought. They will, they will. . . .

At dawn he was carried to the hospital of the French nuns outside the city. A surgeon bandaged the gash in his leg. It was a bad wound, the surgeon said, but it would heal. They placed him on a cot. He would not lie down, but sat propped on pillows, his pistol primed and cocked in his hand, his sword on the coverlet. He sat and watched the door, his face distorted with anguish, his eyes hot and fevered.

A major from Montgomery's column was brought in, bleeding and pale.

"Well, have we seized the fort?" Arnold asked hoarsely.

"No," the major said. "No—and never will, Colonel Arnold. We're beaten."

"I don't believe it!"

"It's true, sir."

"Where is Montgomery?"

"Dead. Killed in the first British counterfire. Most of his men retreated in panic. I stayed—and got this riddled shoulder."

Arnold shuddered. "But *my* men? And Morgan?"

"Morgan surrendered—"

"No! I *won't* believe it!"

"He had to, sir," the major said. "Morgan was overwhelmed. He wept with rage when they cornered him. He begged them to shoot him. They preferred to make him a prisoner. He wouldn't give the Britishers his sword; finally he handed it to a French priest who was hearing the prayers of the dying."

Arnold bowed his head. "No! Oh, no!" Then he muttered: "Oswald? What of Oswald?"

"Captured."

"My other officers? They didn't surrender?"

"Yes, nearly all, sir. Those who weren't killed outright had no choice but to do so. We were beaten before we started," the major said. "It was never a surprise attack. Spies betrayed us."

Arnold gritted his teeth in silent agony.

By noon he knew the worst. Of the men he had led into the Lower Town forty-eight were dead, thirty-four wounded, three hundred and seventy-two captured. Many of the survivors had fled toward Montreal—or deserted entirely. Montgomery's force had been almost wiped out.

The casualties of the British, both in killed and wounded, were only twenty. . . .

Unbelievable—yet true. And still Benedict Arnold would not relinquish his determination to take the mighty fortress! Now, with Montgomery gone, he was in sole charge at Quebec. There were some shreds of an army dotted about on the St. Lawrence shore. He would gather the shreds and weave them into strength.

He wrote to Montreal asking the Americans there for assistance. He wrote hopefully to Washington asking for more troops. He wrote to Hannah:

> I have no thought of leaving this proud town, until I first enter it in triumph. I know you will be anxious for me. That Providence which has carried me through so many dangers is still my protection. I am in the way of duty and know no fear.

From his hospital bed he issued orders. When he was able to be up, hobbling on a cane, he supervised the encamping of his little army around the lower walls. Quebec, he said, was in a state of siege. The siege would not be lifted. He had parceled out his scant stores of food. He told the men they must tighten their belts. They would be fed—though meagerly!—while help was being sent.

It was ridiculous, of course, impractical—the mere handful of half-starved Americans, chilled to their very bones, ragged and battle scarred, proposing to keep a much larger force shut up in a fortified town. But it was somehow noble, too. And somehow they accomplished it. The British did not swoop down to destroy them. The British and the French inhabitants crouched behind their high walls.

Assistance from Montreal was slow in coming; it dribbled in, small detachments of men, small allotments of meat, meal and ammunition. The Americans who occupied Montreal were having their own troubles—fending off the enemy, repulsing hostile Indians. But the colonists and the Continental Congress had been astonished and distressed by the bad news from Canada. Regiments were being raised and supplies voted for Arnold's relief.

Meantime, Arnold was receiving news of a different sort that delighted him. For his valor and perseverance he had been promoted to the rank of brigadier general. Congress had expressed its appreciation for his wonderful march from Cambridge to Quebec, and for all his "spirited exertions" in the patriot cause. Washington had spoken of him in glowing, grateful terms and called him "the intrepid and enterprising Arnold."

So he wasn't too dissatisfied with his situation—until David Wooster arrived April 1 with reinforcements.

Wooster had been commanding at Montreal. Arnold wished that he had stayed there. Oh, he remembered Wooster. Yes, indeed! He remembered the day when Wooster, as a selectman, had not wanted to give him the keys to the New Haven powder house. Arnold thought of Wooster as a bungling old duffer who might be scheming to supplant him here—at any rate, to divide the leadership.

Wooster seemed harmless. Nevertheless Arnold was suspicious and jealous of him. Wooster had written to Washington: "When told hereafter, Colonel Arnold's amazing story will scarcely be credited."

"I will not tolerate Wooster!" Arnold said and he requested a transfer to Montreal. The request was granted.

Perhaps, leaving Quebec, he was somewhat regretful. He had not entered the proud city in triumph, and perhaps he thought of Natanis' pronouncement: "The wilderness will yield to the Dark Eagle, but the Rock will defy him."

But the experience had been rewarding. Honor, distinction, praise, these meant something. Perhaps they meant more than anything else.

11

THE AMERICAN ADMIRAL

AFTER HIS FIRST FEW WEEKS IN MONTREAL, ARNOLD BEGAN TO feel that the American campaign in Canada was doomed. The Canadian people seemed to have no desire to form a fourteenth American colony. He heard that Sir Guy Carleton, with hundreds of fresh troops from England, had driven the little American force away from Quebec and would soon move on Montreal.

Arnold did not think he could defend Montreal against Carleton. He had only a handful of men; an epidemic of smallpox was sweeping the town, and all roundabout were hordes of the most blood-thirsty Indians, whom the British had bribed to support them. Also he was having trouble with the officers on his staff. Time and again he argued and wrangled with one or another of them, even challenging them to duels. He knew he was not popular with his subordinates—well, it was their fault, he thought, never his!

He wrote to General John Sullivan, who was trying to push back bands of Indian marauders on the Sorel River. "Let us quit and secure our own country," he said to Sullivan, "before it is too late." And he wrote to General Horatio Gates, commanding at Ticonderoga, that if Carleton struck at Montreal, the Americans would be wise to retreat southward to Lake Champlain.

In June he learned that Carleton was coming up the St. Lawrence with an enormous army.

"We'll hold the town as long as we can," he said, and he stationed young Captain James Wilkinson in a barge on the river to watch for the redcoats.

"Notify me the minute you see the British boats," he told Wilkinson.

The very next day Wilkinson hastened to Arnold's headquarters.

"They're coming!" Wilkinson cried. "I've seen them!"

Within two hours Arnold had his company out of the Montreal fort, marching for St. Johns on the Sorel, marching fast and destroying bridges and roads as they went. General Sullivan and his Indian fighters were at St. Johns.

"I know this village," Arnold said to Sullivan. "A year ago I raided it and got an enemy sloop here. What a night it was!" He smiled at the memory. "Well, sir, we must burn St. Johns and cross to that island yonder."

By evening the village was in ruins. Wilkinson had stolen a horse for Arnold and one for himself. Side by side they trotted through the smoldering streets to the waterfront, where the piers and warehouses were charred and blackened. Sullivan and his men were crossing in bateaux to the island. Arnold ordered his men into the boats.

Wilkinson dismounted. "I have a skiff and some Indian paddlers for you, General Arnold."

Arnold still sat astride his horse, a beautiful roan, sleek and graceful. "Not yet, Captain," he said.

There were noises in the distance. "We're pursued!" Wilkinson exclaimed.

"Oh, yes, they'll pursue us all the way. Are you frightened?"

"No, sir." But the noises were louder, a thumping of hoofs, a clatter of sabers. "I think they're close," Wilkinson said. "Quite close."

Arnold got down from the saddle. "Captain, I was the first American to invade Canada. I shall be the last to leave it." Lifting his pistol, he shot his horse between the eyes. The animal whinnied once, then crashed to the ground, quivering, dying. "Do as I have done, Captain. Shoot your horse."

Wilkinson gasped. "Sir, if you please—it is such a fine creature—"

"And you don't want Carleton to have it."

Wilkinson hesitated. "General Arnold—"

"I command you!"

Wilkinson fired and the second horse dropped dead.

"Now into the skiff, Captain."

They stepped into the skiff. With arms folded dramatically, Arnold stood looking back at the embers of the devastated village, a sturdy, indomitable figure silhouetted against a pall of smoke.

"Row for the island," he said to the paddlers.

The Americans retreated to Ticonderoga, and Arnold conferred with Gates. He said that Carleton would come to Lake Champlain and, if not stopped, would take the American forts and go on to slash through the country below, ripping it apart.

"We must stop him, sir!"

"Stop him?" Gates repeated. "Yes, but how?"

"With our fleet."

Gates smiled. "Our fleet? It consists of a schooner, the St. Johns sloop you captured, several Indian dugouts and a pretty little sailboat."

"We can build a fleet. We must!"

"General Arnold," Gates said frankly, "I am completely ignorant of maritime affairs. But you are somewhat familiar with them—and I want to stop Carleton. Write to General Washington. If the commander in chief approves your idea, I promise you my help."

It was early July, 1776, when Arnold wrote to Washington. On July 4, the American colonies had declared their independence. Henceforth they would be known to the world as the United States of America; and France had agreed to aid the new nation with money and materials of war. But even so, the conflict might drag on for months, years. The Canadian venture had been horribly expensive—more than five thousand men killed either in battle or by disease.

Considering all these circumstances, and dreading an enemy assault from the north, Washington answered Arnold's letter and approved the building of a fleet on Lake Champlain.

Arnold went at the project with all his characteristic vigor. He scoured the neighborhood for axmen, blacksmiths, metal workers. He employed three hundred carpenters, bought canvas, cordage, nails, hawsers and anchors.

Gates helped, as he had promised. Gates hired the crews—and they were mostly landlubbers, for trained sailors were not to be found. But Gates gave Arnold free rein and did not interfere with him.

"In these maritime affairs," he said, "General Arnold is the supreme commander."

By October Arnold had two small schooners, two sloops, four big rowboats, or galleys, and eight of the flat barges called gondolas. Though all were awkward and overweighted with guns, Arnold felt they would serve him well. As each one was finished, he sailed it from the shipyard at Skenesborough to Ticonderoga for Gates to inspect and admire.

He was sure now that Carleton was coming. Information sifted in. It was said that Carleton had many scows, gunboats, longboats and gondolas. His ship, the *Inflexible,* was so large that it had to be dismantled, carried in sections through the rapids of the Sorel River, then rebuilt at St. Johns. And Carleton's crews were not landlubbers. His seven hundred men and their officers were veterans of the Royal Navy.

"Never mind all that," Arnold said. "He can't defeat us!"

In his flagship, the *Congress,* Arnold led his fleet to a cove on the west side of Valcour Island. He knew that Carleton's ships, emerging from the Sorel, would have to pass through the channel just east of Valcour. He would not attempt an open attack, but would pick off the British vessels, one by one, as they appeared in the channel.

"A cat-and-mouse game," he told Gates. "Except that this mouse is much bigger than the cat!"

The morning of October 11, the British ships were seen, under full sail, banners streaming in the wind, and escorted by a thousand Indians in war canoes. Arnold sent out a schooner and four galleys with his heaviest guns to fire on the giant *Inflexible*. As the American cannons roared, all of Carleton's fleet advanced against the wind toward Arnold's cove.

By noon the battle was raging, and for seven hours Lake Champlain resounded with the turmoil. Guns bellowed, masts snapped and splintered, sails flapped and sagged. On the decks powder-stained men shouted as they loaded their weapons, or moaned as they slumped down in pools of blood. From the shore the Indians flashed volley on volley of bullets and a rain of arrows.

The *Inflexible* and the *Congress* fought like two gladiators in an arena. Arnold directed the fire from his flagship. Energetic and resolute, he darted from gun to gun. He saw that a British gondola and two galleys were wrecked. His own losses, he thought, were about the same; his crews were unflinching.

At sunset the British bombardment slacked, the ships moved back out of range. The wind veered and fog drifted over the lake in eddying wisps, then in enveloping clouds.

The *Congress* had been hit in numerous places. Scowling, Arnold examined the punctures. Sixty of his men were dead or wounded. The barrels of ammunition had been scraped to the bottom—and tomorrow Carleton would return, as strong and fierce as ever!

Well, it was time to retire and reorganize.

He ordered that a single lantern be lighted in the stern of each boat, oars muffled, and no more sail hoisted than was absolutely necessary for slow headway. Cloaked by the fog, his fleet eased southward, a silent procession with the *Congress* at the rear.

Twelve miles south of Valcour at a smaller island they anchored. The next day he set the men to plugging the leaking hulls and mending the torn rigging. Two of the gondolas were shattered and had to be sunk; a galley and a sloop were almost beyond repair.

That night they went farther south, to Split Rock. There, in the morning, they were overtaken by Carleton, who had been frantically searching for them. As before, the *Congress* was the Britishers' main target; after two more hours of cannonading Arnold realized that his flagship could not be kept afloat.

But never, never would he let the *Congress* fall to Carleton!

He ordered the helmsman to steer for an inlet. When the ship grounded, he ordered the crew off.

"Fire her!" he cried. "Put the torch to her!"

Flame spurted and spread, consuming the *Congress*.

The other American vessels drew in toward the inlet.

"Put the torch to them all!" Arnold ordered.

Soon all were blazing and the crews were off and firing a last round of rifleshots at their pursuers.

Into the shelter of the forest Arnold led his men, along the trail to Ticonderoga. They reached the fort October 15. For three days they had not eaten or slept; they were exhausted and haggard.

And if they had not vanquished Carleton, they had stopped him. Eight months would elapse before the British again came down Lake Champlain. Arnold's little fleet had waged the first naval battle in the history of the United States. Benedict Arnold would be known as the first American admiral.

12

DISAPPOINTMENT

IN NOVEMBER ARNOLD LEFT TICONDEROGA AND STARTED FOR New Haven to visit his little sons and Hannah. The time was convenient for such a trip. Carleton had hovered about Crown Point for several weeks, then wheeled back toward Canada. The American defenses of Lake Champlain would be safe for a while. General Gates had moved to Albany, New York, and General Arthur St. Clair had replaced him.

Arnold rode through crisp autumn weather to Albany, breaking his journey there. He had business in Albany. Two men had been spreading evil reports of him. He must confront his critics and answer them.

One was Major John Brown, a friend of Ethan Allen's who had accompanied that brawny mountaineer to Ticonderoga in May, 1775. Brown was also a crony of James Easton's. Brown had seen Arnold kick and berate Easton and order him from the fort premises. He had complained often and harshly about Benedict Arnold. Now he was insisting that Gates arrest Arnold and have him tried by a military court for thirteen "crimes." To Brown it seemed that almost every act of Arnold's career as a soldier had been a crime. The latest crime, Brown said, was the loss of the new American fleet through Arnold's "great misconduct."

Colonel Moses Hazen, Arnold's other foe, had been associated with him at Montreal, where they had disagreed violently about the purchase of army supplies. Hazen said that Arnold had accused him of stealing; this had injured Hazen's reputation. He asked for a military court which would clear him and rebuke his accuser.

Gates not only refused to arrest Arnold; he curtly dismissed Major Brown, telling him that most Americans were pleased at the result of the battle on Lake Champlain. Very indignant, Brown stamped out of Albany, swearing revenge—he would lay his charges and the "crimes" before the Congress! But the court-martial called to look into Hazen's claims ruled that Arnold had, indeed, been guilty of injuring the reputation of an innocent man.

Both cases were aired in the newspapers and gossiped about; and when Arnold, too, stamped out of Albany, he was in a very bad humor. . . . Why was it that he had so many personal enemies? Why was he nagged by quarrels, petty persecutions? He felt positive that he was never to blame!

But as he traveled through Connecticut, his anger vanished. Here he was hailed as a hero—the successful leader of that wilderness pilgrimage, the builder and commander of that spunky midget navy. He saw some of the men who had marched with him to Quebec; they had been released by the British in an exchange of prisoners. They cheered and waved their hats at him. He saw Eleazar Oswald—sensible, clever Eleazar, who fondly clapped him on the shoulder.

Best of all was his meeting with his family. The three boys had grown so much, they were so handsome. They crowded around their famous father, eagerly admiring his sword and scabbard. They scrambled into his lap to listen to enchanting tales of Indians, scouting and warfare.

And Hannah was herself, smiling and steadfast. In the evenings, when she had tucked the boys into bed, Hannah sat with him in the parlor. It was quite like old times, wasn't it? He could almost imagine that they were back in the old house at Norwich, Hannah sewing by lamplight, logs crimson on the hearth, the room warm and hushed around them, winter darkness at the windows.

Watching Hannah, he thought that she was still, at thirty-five, a pretty woman, tall and graceful and blond. She would have made some lucky fellow an excellent wife. It was odd that, except for her brief, absurd interest in that jigging Frenchman, she had never seemed to want a beau.

Of course, she would never marry now. . . .

And just as well, he thought—for how could he have managed without her?

She asked him about Major Brown and Colonel Hazen. "Why did they say those dreadful things, Benedict?"

"Oh, because of trifling incidents in the past."

"Perhaps you flew into a temper and antagonized them?"

"Perhaps, Hannah. I don't know."

She nodded. "People have the habit of remembering trifling incidents—as they remember being stung by a wasp. And they seldom forgive the wasp. You must learn to curb your temper. You must be careful. A man with the eyes of the world upon him must be *extra* good."

He smiled amiably at the gentle scolding and said he had never been otherwise.

He left New Haven for Boston early in February. Eleazar Oswald was going to Boston that day. They drove together in a sleigh over snow-packed roads. The weather was cold and bright; the sleigh bells jingled musically.

They talked at length of the war. The British now occupied New York City. After a series of hard-fought battles, Washington had retreated to winter quarters at Morristown to rest his brave, tired regiments. In the spring the conflict would begin again; for the present there was an interval of quiet.

Oswald spoke of Quebec, of their comrades in the attack and siege.

"John Lamb is in Connecticut now," Oswald said. "He wants to recruit an artillery battalion. I've told him to count on me."

"Lamb? He was captured with you, wasn't he? Colonel Lamb, I recall him as a rough, gruff, effective soldier," Arnold said.

"Yes, and he can get the men for his outfit. But he hasn't the money to arm them. Nor have I."

Arnold slapped the reins; the sleigh bells sang. "I could lend Lamb a thousand dollars. Would that be enough?"

"I think so."

"Tell Lamb I'll lend it to him. But on one condition, Eleazar: you must be the lieutenant colonel of Colonel Lamb's outfit."

Oswald grinned. "You're a true friend—and a true patriot. The rumor is that you're due for another promotion. Major General Arnold, eh? Nobody deserves it more!"

"Well, I'm in line for it," Arnold said. "And just between ourselves, I expect it. Why not? I'm the oldest of the brigadiers and I've had the most favorable notice. I think I'm the most capable. Washington seems to think that, too. And the British—do you know that in London my picture is displayed on the streets, in shops, as the best of the American officers, the one most to be feared?"

"I can believe it," Eleazar said.

"Yes, when Congress makes its next batch of major generals, I'll probably head the list. And superior in rank to those elevated with me—I'll see to that also! Yes, it will happen, it's bound to happen. It's in the cards!" He paused, flushed and excited.

"The Dark Eagle," Eleazar murmured softly, glancing at him, the stern hawklike profile, the strong blunt chin. "The Dark Eagle. Nations will behold him and sound his praises."

In spite of the war, Boston was lively and rather gay. Arnold was not sorry to be there. Since the evacuation of the British, many American officers had been stationed in the city, some had brought their wives and children. Arnold bought a fine new uniform of blue and buff, white silk stockings, a pair of those elegant buckled shoes he always fancied. He went to entertainments and dinners. He was introduced to beautiful young ladies, danced with them and paid them polite compliments.

But constantly, whatever he did, he thought of the recognition soon to be his. Major General Arnold! Why was Congress so slow? When would the promotions be announced?

They were announced February 19. Five major generals were appointed. And Benedict Arnold was not among them.

He was immeasurably shocked, then seething with fury.

He stared at the names listed in the newspapers. Not one of the five men—not one!—was his equal in experience or accomplishments.

He had been passed over, basely and inexcusably insulted.

At Morristown, Washington was reading the newspapers with the same astonishment. Washington hadn't been consulted, but he had not doubted that Arnold would be promoted. Now he thought that a mistake had been made, in omitting Arnold's name from the list.

He wrote to Arnold, begging him not to take any hasty steps. Surely the mistake would be corrected. He wrote to Congress. Surely, he said, Congress must know that Arnold was valuable—there was no more active and spirited officer in its army.

"It is not to be presumed," said Washington, "that he will continue in service under such a slight."

Still bewildered, Arnold replied to his commander in chief. He said he would not take any hasty steps. But perhaps Congress wanted to be rid of him, and this was a means of making him resign? He mentioned his devotion to his country, how he had repeatedly fought and bled and risked his life in battle.

"I am conscious of the rectitude of my intentions. Where have I failed? Let me go before Congress and be questioned. Let a court of inquiry investigate me."

After two unhappy weeks he wrote again to Washington. The humiliation was more than he could stand If he could not go to Philadelphia and demand an explanation from Congress, he would resign.

Nothing could have been kinder than Washington's response; it expressed the deepest concern and friendship. Washington himself had asked Congress for an explanation. He had been told that the promotions were apportioned according to the size of each state, the number of soldiers each state furnished to the army. Connecticut, a small state, already had two major generals, which was its rightful portion. Therefore General Arnold could not now be raised in rank.

Washington was surprised, he had not known about this rule, he did not like it. But Congress, he said, was a public body and could place or displace at pleasure. He thought Arnold should not go to Philadelphia.

"As no particular charge is alleged against you, I do not see how you can demand a court of inquiry. . . . I hope you will choose to remain in military service. But your own feelings must be your guide."

So it was not a mistake at all! Benedict Arnold had been deliberately embarrassed. His own feelings? They were stark rage and desperately hurt pride. Whether or not Washington believed it to be useless, he would go to Philadelphia.

In April he set out—and on the way was sidetracked.

There was fighting in Connecticut. Led by William Tryon, the British governor of New York, two thousand enemy troopers had sailed along the coast to Compo beach near Norwalk, where they hid their boats and marched to Danbury, raiding and burning the town. As they fled back to Compo, they were harried by gallant little companies of American militiamen.

When Arnold heard of the Danbury raid, he went immediately to help the militiamen. He found them at Redding and took command of the chase. Much of it was skirmishing, but a battle occurred at Ridgefield, and Arnold was in the thick of it. His horse went down, struck by nine bullets. As he pulled his feet loose from the stirrups a British soldier lunged at him with a bayonet.

"I've got you! You're my prisoner."

"Not yet," Arnold said quietly, and drew his pistol and shot the man dead.

At Compo, Colonel John Lamb's brand-new artillery unit met the raiders. Arnold saw Eleazar, as Lamb's second in command, shelling the beach. Cannons growled, bullets pelted and whined. Again Arnold jumped from the saddle, as the horse he rode was killed. Ducking a barrage from redcoat rifles, he rallied his men.

But the British were weary. They had been fired at from every fence corner and stone wall and grove of trees. They scurried for their boats, tumbled in and made off.

Arnold greeted Eleazar heartily. "Lieutenant Colonel Oswald, eh?"

"Yes, sir!" Eleazar laughed. "Tryon is a bully. He had four times as many lads—and we licked him. Hey, Benedict! Your collar's in tatters."

"My collar, not my neck," Arnold said. "They didn't touch me."

The punishment of the Danbury raiders attracted a great deal of comment, and Benedict Arnold was given most of the credit for it. On May 2, Congress appointed him a major general. But the rank he coveted, seniority over those major generals named three months earlier, was withheld.

And why was this? he asked himself. The promotion did not satisfy him. He wanted the higher rank, too. Why was Congress so stingy?

Besides, John Brown was busily maligning him everywhere. Brown would not be silenced. He was printing and distributing handbills in the eastern cities. Arnold was a criminal, the handbills said in bold black type.

"Money is this man's god, and to get enough of it he would sacrifice his country!" shrieked the handbills.

Arnold went to Morristown and talked with Washington.

"It is not to be endured," he said. "Now Congress *must* investigate my record and character. My rank must be restored. I am going to Philadelphia!"

And now Washington consented.

"Yes, you are justified in going," Washington said, and he sent a letter to Congress recommending Arnold and praising him unstintingly.

Washington was not alone in believing that Arnold had been slandered. Other military leaders and statesmen believed it. And when at last Congress looked into his military record, nothing really wrong was found with it.

But Congress had granted him a very large sum of money for the Quebec expedition, thousands of dollars with which to buy equipment, provisions; and he could account for only one-sixth of the sum. How had the remainder been spent?

His answer was that he had not handled the money himself, or not all of it. His staff officers had bought many things. He had relied on them to jot down their expenditures. Perhaps they had forgotten; perhaps they were not accurate bookkeepers. Also, some of his official papers, contained in boxes, had been on his flagship; unfortunately, the boxes of papers were destroyed with the ship on Lake Champlain.

He offered no further reason for the errors in his accounts. He asserted then, as always, that he was perfectly honest, the most conscientious man on earth! . . .

Was he? Were these errors to be traced simply to inaccurate bookkeeping, his own or somebody else's? Or had he wastefully frittered away funds belonging to the government, the taxpayers, the people?

There was a much worse possibility: *had he pocketed the money for himself?*

The Congressmen debated solemnly.

In the end they declared that John Brown had "cruelly

and groundlessly" besmirched General Arnold's character and conduct. It was voted that a horse be procured and given to General Arnold as a token of esteem for repulsing the Danbury raiders, when two mounts had been shot from under him.

But his rank as a senior major general was still withheld.

A horse! Wrath choked him, he could not speak. He had been lied about, cheated, shamed. He had asked only for an honor earned many times over.

And they gave him a horse!

Perhaps it was then that a bleak and terrible thought first swam into his mind—a thought he instantly pushed aside, but one which would come again and finally haunt him.

On July11, he resigned from the army.

Before his resignation could be accepted by Congress there were alarming reports. A huge British force, aided by Loyalists and Indians, was descending from Canada. General John Burgoyne headed the force. "Gentleman Johnny," he was called, a man to be reckoned with. His purpose was to do what Carleton had attempted: to split New England in two, to conquer by dividing.

Washington informed Congress of the danger. It was grave, very grave. Burgoyne must be checked. An American force, the "Northern Army," was gathering at Fort Edward, near the town of Saratoga, New York. General Schuyler would command it; later General Gates would take command. But Washington also wanted an especially judicious and brave officer to lead on the militia.

He wanted Benedict Arnold.

Arnold dashed off a note to Congress, requesting that his resignation be held up, not considered until this service was behind him. In a few days he was traveling north, rejoicing at the prospect of work, action—and probably glory.

13

DANGER FROM THE NORTH

GENERAL PHILIP SCHUYLER SAID THAT ENGLAND WAS BECOMING serious about the war and meant to win it in a minimum of time. England was throwing everything she had into the effort.

"Burgoyne!" Schuyler said. "Burgoyne with eight thousand troops, fifteen hundred horses, a baggage train from here to yonder—he plans to deal the decisive, fatal blow."

Arnold had just reached Fort Edward and was conferring with Schuyler. They were well acquainted. Schuyler was middle-aged, tall, aristocratic in looks and manner. Arnold respected him, but thought he was a little slow, a little too cautious.

"And St. Clair abandoned Ticonderoga to Burgoyne?"

"Yes," Schuyler said. "Gentleman Johnny then nabbed our forts below. Now he'll float his men and truck in barges down Lake George, forge through the woods and go on to Albany, either by land or water."

"Is Albany his goal? He'll never get there."

"I hope not, Arnold. If so, he'll make connection with Sir Henry Clinton's regiments marching up from New York City."

"We can't allow that," Arnold said. "Have you told me all the bad news?"

No, Schuyler answered. Colonel Barry St. Leger was rampaging through the Mohawk Valley with a mixed army of British regulars, Loyalists and Indians. Joseph Brant commanded the Indians. Brant was the foremost chief of the Mohawk tribes. He had been educated at an English school in Connecticut, and had fought for England in the French and

Indian War. His Indian name was Thayendanegea; translated, this was Bundle of Sticks, signifying *strength*.

Recently St. Leger and Brant had besieged Fort Stanwix in the valley. When a company of militia went to rescue the garrison of Stanwix, a ghastly battle occurred in the forest near the fort.

"The Indians ruthlessly scalped and butchered their captives," Schuyler said. "Women and children were not spared. I predict the British will regret the day they ever made allies of Brant's barbarians."

People in the Stanwix region had been particularly horrified by the murder of Jane McCrea, a lovely young girl who was engaged to marry one of Burgoyne's Loyalist officers.

"She was seized and scalped, anyway," Schuyler said. "A beastly thing! I'm told that Burgoyne blanched pale as milk when he heard of it. But the savages are quite out of hand, drunk with bloodshed. Since Jane McCrea's tragedy many farmers and homesteaders who were Loyalists are flocking to us for protection. I suppose they feel that nobody is safe."

"Fort Stanwix hasn't yet been relieved?"

"No," Schuyler said. "It should be, to prevent another massacre. But our immediate duty, Arnold, is to check Burgoyne."

During the next week Schuyler and Arnold worked to obstruct Burgoyne's progress. Hundreds of axmen went into the woods and chopped down trees to stack in the path of the enemy. Logs and brush were rolled up as barriers, bridges were burned. Still, Gentleman Johnny came on; each day scouts brought word of him.

Arnold was impatient. Could nothing more be done?

Then, one rainy August night, a wet and wan soldier staggered into the American camp. It was Colonel Marinus Willett from Stanwix. Somehow Willett had stolen through St. Leger's lines and walked for miles in the rain to plead for help. The Indians were closing in around the fort; the starving inmates would soon be brutally slaughtered.

"I'll send help," Schuyler said. "What's the size of St. Leger's villianous mob? Two thousand? I can send about nine hundred men—with a volunteer commander."

Arnold leaped to his feet. "Let me tackle the job."

"I was thinking of one of the brigadiers," Schuyler said.

Arnold insisted. "No, I'm your volunteer."

With his nine hundred men he traversed the Mohawk Valley to a plain called the German Flats and halted there. It was Loyalist territory; some of the inhabitants were plotting an uprising against the Americans. Arnold made prisoners of the conspirators. If the people of the German Flats were easily scared, as had been said—well, he would scare them!

He issued a ferocious proclamation, addressing St. Leger and his Loyalist and redskin allies as bandits, robbers, cutthroats and traitors. They must lay down their arms within ten days, or they would all be treated as Jane McCrea was treated—and no mercy shown them.

His officers thought the proclamation was unwise.

He smiled. "Don't worry. I have something up my sleeve."

He interviewed the Loyalist prisoners. One was an awkward, foolish youth named Hon-Yost Schuyler, who for years had associated with the Mohawk tribes, hunting and fishing with them. Hon-Yost had the body of a full-grown man, the brain of a child; he was a simpleton.

His mother came to Arnold, begging for his life.

"My son is not normal," the woman said. "It is because of this that the Indians are kind to him. The Indians think that the Great Spirit guides and cares for the insane, the half-witted. Do not kill Hon-Yost!"

"If he obeys me," Arnold said, "he will not be killed."

The woman wept. "Yes, yes! He will obey you in anything, everything. I promise! My poor boy, he is entirely harmless."

Arnold ordered Hon-Yost to remove the coat he wore. He riddled the coat with bullet holes and had Hon-Yost put it on again. He told him to go to Fort Stanwix and warn St. Leger's Indians that enormous hordes of Americans were approaching, St. Leger would be overwhelmed.

But Arnold was not sure that Hon-Yost was entirely harmless. In the neighborhood were a few Oneida Indians, who were known to be friendly to the Americans. Arnold selected a stalwart Oneida and set him on Hon-Yost's trail.

"Watch him," he said to the Oneida. "See that he obeys my orders."

To Hon-Yost's mother, Arnold said: "You have another son? Nicholas? While Hon-Yost is away, Nicholas will be held as a hostage."

St. Leger's Indians were dismayed when Hon-Yost burst into their midst, babbling and trembling, pointing to the holes in his coat. They asked him about the Americans. *"How many?"*

Hon-Yost pointed to the leaves of the trees.

"When are the Americans coming?"

"In twenty-four hours," Hon-Yost said. "In twenty-four hours."

The Indians were panic-stricken; they yelled and whooped. Roused by the tumult, St. Leger summoned Hon-Yost to his tent, and Hon-Yost repeated his incoherent, frightening story. Then the Oneida appeared.

"It is so," the Oneida told St. Leger. "They are as leaves of the trees. In twenty-four hours they will swarm upon you."

St. Leger went out to speak to his Indians. He tried to calm them, but they would not listen. Thoroughly terrified, they were deserting him—and carrying off his supplies. The Loyalists, too, were deserting; lastly, the British regulars scampered to hide themselves in the forest.

The Oneida reported to General Arnold that his ruse had succeeded beyond all expectation. In the confusion of the flight, the Indians had knifed and tomahawked dozens of the scattering Britishers; St. Leger himself had barely escaped.

Arnold then marched to Stanwix, quickly liberated the inmates of the fort and released Hon-Yost and his brother Nicholas to their mother.

When Arnold returned to the Northern Army, he found it changed. General Gates had replaced Schuyler. Several companies of militia had been added. Daniel Morgan, back in service, was there with his Virginia sharpshooters. And an inspiring message had come from Bennington, Vermont, where the Green Mountain Militia had smartly rebuffed a detachment of Burgoyne's troops.

The Americans were enthusiastic and boastful.

"Burgoyne?" the soldiers said. "We'll give him a proper thumping!"

Arnold was glad to see Morgan again and to stroll with him around the camp.

"Have you recovered from your wound at Quebec?" Morgan asked one day.

A load of ammunition stood at the roadside. Very agilely Arnold vaulted over it, landing lightly, and bowing to Morgan.

"D'you think my leg is not as good as new, Daniel?" he said. "I am in fighting trim!"

Some of Morgan's Virginians were passing by. "Hurray for General Arnold!" they cried.

He laughed and saluted them.

In September General Gates moved the Northern Army to the town of Stillwater. On Bemis Heights he dug entrenchments and erected fortifications. The Americans were now within four miles of Burgoyne and preparing for a battle.

At Ticonderoga, during the building of the fleet, Gates and Arnold had been friends; and in Albany, Gates had been cordial to Arnold when others criticized him. But now there was a coolness between them, and they seemed to clash about everything. Arnold wanted to attack Burgoyne at once. Gates said Burgoyne must make the attack.

Small in stature, bald, with steel-rimmed spectacles spanning his thin nose, Gates had a temper as stubborn as Arnold's. He was as ambitious as Arnold, and he resented the fact that Washington and Schuyler had so much confidence in Arnold's military skill. Here Gates was the supreme commander! He would not forget it, nor would he let Arnold forget it, either.

So Gates waited—and Arnold fussed and fumed.

On September 19, Burgoyne advanced toward Bemis Heights, as if to begin the battle. Gates sent out Arnold with three thousand men. In the cleared fields of Freeman's Farm, the columns met. The British guns opened fire and hammered hard; the Americans firmly held their position. But Arnold saw an opportunity to take the offensive. Spurring his horse, he galloped forward—and heard thundering hoofs, felt his bridle snatched.

It was James Wilkinson, with Gate's order for a retreat.

Arnold hesitated, just as Wilkinson once had done at an amazing order.

"Retreat, Captain Wilkinson?"

"By General Gates's command, sir."

Unwillingly, Arnold retreated. Burgoyne won the day; the British encamped that night at Freeman's Farm.

Arnold rushed to Gates's headquarters. "Why was I called back? I could have finished off Burgoyne right there!" he shouted.

"I feared that by some rash act you might do mischief, General Arnold."

"Mischief! *Mischief*, sir!"

Gates said nothing more; in the dispatch he sent to Washington, Arnold's name did not even appear.

Arnold saw the dispatch and stamped again into headquarters, accusing Gates of gross unfairness.

"I would remind you, sir, that I am a major general—"

"Are you?" Gates asked. "Are you in the army at all? I thought you had resigned."

"General Washington knows my status," Arnold roared. "It's at Washington's wish that I am in the North. If I am not needed, I shall leave!"

"You may leave whenever you like," Gates said. "I'll give you a pass. You are of little consequence to the army anywhere."

Arnold stamped to the tent in which he had his own quarters and wrote a scorching letter, requesting the pass. Yes, he would leave! He would go to Washington's regiments in Pennsylvania. Washington would welcome him.

But by this time the entire American camp knew about the quarrel. The soldiers were perturbed. When they learned that Arnold was packing his kit, they grumbled loudly to their officers. Arnold must stay, they said. Burgoyne was only playing possum; Burgoyne would soon stir—and General Arnold would certainly be needed then!

A petition was drawn up and signed by most of the officers, asking him to reconsider. The enlisted men appealed to him, too. He was flattered and appeased. Smoothing down his ruffled feathers, he said he would stay.

But he was arrogant about it; he couldn't be courteous to Gates. Under the surface, both men were angry and sullen.

On October 7, Burgoyne stirred, marshaling his troops in battle array. Poised and calm, the Americans faced him. They were twelve thousand strong now, their number twice that of Gentleman Johnny's.

Gates instructed the commanders of the various divisions. To Arnold, he said: "You will keep to your tent, sir. Someone else will lead your men."

Hatred gleamed in Arnold's eyes; in silence he turned away.

The battle began in the afternoon. Arnold, in his tent, heard the cannonading, the rattle of musketry. Wretchedly, he lifted the tent flap and peered out. He couldn't see the fighting, but he knew it was hot and desperate—one of the great battles of the war, of history, and he was to have no part in it.

Suddenly he grabbed up his sword, ran out and mounted his horse.

"No man can keep me in a tent this day!" he cried, and dashed onto the field.

Gates was in his headquarters when someone came to tell him that Arnold was out there behaving like a madman. Gates sent a young lieutenant to bring him in.

The lieutenant was to say later that he couldn't locate General Arnold, the smoke was so dense, the noise so deafening, and the lines all intermingled. Perhaps the lieutenant meant that he couldn't catch up with him. For Arnold was a whirlwind of vigor and wild courage, leading an assault in one section, then galloping to another section, another assault there. Everywhere, the men followed him, pressing at Burgoyne with a steady, relentless pounding of guns and artillery. Slowly but surely the British retreated and then were driven to flight.

As enemy rifles fired a final volley, Arnold felt a searing pain in his leg. He was shot, he fell heavily, shouting to the men around him: "Go on! Rush on!"

But the battle was ending, the guns stilled.

At sunset four of his men came with a litter of poles and blankets. They bent over him. "Where are you hit, General Arnold?"

"My leg," he muttered. "The same leg, my Quebec leg. . . . I wish it had been my heart."

14

THE NEW POST

BURGOYNE FORMALLY SURRENDERED OCTOBER 15, IN THE TOWN of Saratoga—and though it was General Gates who received his sword, everyone knew that General Benedict Arnold had been the real hero of the battle on Bemis Heights.

Impossible now to keep Arnold's name out of dispatches and bulletins. The country rang with it; this was his great moment of fame.

And, as he had foreseen, the battle was of great importance. It sent American hopes soaring and had tremendous effect abroad. England had failed to crush her rebellious colonies with one stunning blow; therefore she sought a reconciliation with them. A British agent went to Paris to confer with two American agents, Benjamin Franklin and Silas Deane. England would make peace—providing, of course, that Americans remained subjects of the English king.

The proposal was rejected. Americans stood squarely for independence!

France then formally recognized the independence of the United States, the first foreign nation to do so. As an ally, France would send troops to America and would be at war on the seas with England.

For a long time Arnold was in the military hospital at Albany, for this second wound to his leg was far worse than the first. He thought it would never heal, and he blamed the doctors and surgeons, shouting that they were pretenders and all in league against him. It was spring before he could walk on a crutch to the carriage which would take him home. He had to travel slowly and did not arrive in New Haven until May 4.

But, oh, what a marvelous day that was, perhaps the brightest in his life! His old company of Guards, in full regalia, ushered him into town with fifes and drums. Cannons boomed a salute; the citizens of New Haven thronged the streets; and behind his carriage paraded all the militiamen from miles around.

Hannah and his sons embraced him. Leaning on the shoulders of young Benedict and Richard, he went into his house and sank into a chair.

"I shall always limp, boys," he said, "always be a bit lame. The doctors were very clumsy."

Hannah smiled. "I'll wager you were a difficult invalid."

"Well, those sawbones should have had me up and about two months earlier. Naturally I cursed them—for their stupidity."

"And Congress has given you that seniority in rank you wanted, Father?" said young Benedict.

"Yes, Ben. I have General Washington to thank for it."

Henry, who was five, reverently fingered the gilt buttons on his father's uniform. "Did you curse the soldier who shot you?"

"No, Henry. The chap was only doing his duty. He was a German lad, one of the Hessians hired by the British. Not much taller than our Ben. I told my comrades to spare him, and they did."

"Can you stay with us now, Father?"

"For a week or two. Then I'll go to my new post, wherever it is. General Washington will assign me."

"When will the war be over?"

"I don't know, Henry. My dearest wish is that it will be over soon."

"I think it will," Richard said. "Aunt Hannah thinks it will, now that France is on our side."

"The French alliance, eh?" Arnold glanced at Hannah. "Well, I myself have never rated France very highly, or the French, any of them. Have I, Hannah?"

"No," she said. "I remember."

It was good to be at home, but he was restless and he felt his lameness keenly. And he knew that his dearest wish was not for the war to be over. It must not end too abruptly—not until he had played a principal role in the drama. But what would his role be? What could a lame man do to win fame and glory?

As he sat at the window, basking in the mellow May sunshine, he looked out upon his wharves and warehouses. They were idle, also. With trade regulations so binding, there was little shipping; his merchant vessels were rotting away. And the drugshop? Its shelves were nearly empty; no drugs to be imported now from England, from anywhere; no beautiful books or other luxury items. But who would have bought them? People were so poor, money so scarce. The country was in the pinch of poverty; trade had been strangled by the war.

And yet occasionally a ship from Europe glided into an American port with a cargo of luxuries. It was illegal, but it was done. There were still people to buy the contraband stuff, too, at fantastic prices. Yes, a few people still had gold and silver coins hoarded secretly for just such purchases. They were the people who turned the war to their advantage. Profiteers!

How wrong it was that some Americans should be enriched by the suffering and unselfishness of others!

He thought of the fortune he might have made, had not the war intervened. He was shrewd at business. Suppose he had not sacrificed his business for the sake of his country? He would be wealthy now, a really wealthy man. And as it was, he had nothing. Or almost nothing. Yes, not only had he not *made* money—actually he had lost a lot. And that was wrong. . . .

"Benedict," Hannah said, behind him. "Your supper, Benedict."

"Oh, very well," he replied. But he had no appetite, he wasn't hungry.

A letter came from Washington. The commander in chief was sending General Arnold a gift of epaulets and sword knots, and he wanted him to visit Valley Forge, Pennsylvania, where the Eastern Army had wintered.

Hannah read the letter. "See!" she cried. "At the bottom of the page, General Washington says that he is 'affectionately' yours. What a wonderful word it is—*affectionately!*"

He drove to Valley Forge in General Henry Knox's coach with Mrs. Knox, who was going to join her husband there. Arnold had known Mrs. Knox in Boston; she was a pleasant traveling companion. The coach was comfortable, but plain. Arnold reflected that he'd have to buy a conveyance of some sort, now that he was lame and couldn't ride a horse. A coach or a chaise. . . .

He thought suddenly of Dr. Daniel Lathrop's brass-studded chaise in Norwich, how proud he had felt to ride in it. But a coach was more appropriate for him now; he would have one—and a fine one. He liked fine things; they suited him. Though he never drank to excess, he relished a glass of fine wine to sip with his meals. He liked to wear fine clothes and to have servants about him.

As they bowled along, Mrs. Knox spoke of the pitiable conditions in Valley Forge this past winter, the awful privations of the soldiers—the men famishing for food, threadbare in the freezing cold, many of them shoeless, their numbed feet wrapped in rags which made bloody imprints on the snow. They had seemed to exist on faith alone, faith in God, the patriot ideals and George Washington.

And Mrs. Washington had helped to sustain them, too. Yes, Mrs. Washington had been with the General all winter, working day after day at the most humble chores—cooking sewing, nursing the sick, caring for the destitute.

But in Philadelphia, said Mrs. Knox, conditions had been quite the opposite. Since last September the British had occupied Philadelphia—the Continental Congress hastily picking up and leaving just before Sir William Howe marched in.

"Philadelphia is a nest of Loyalists. They *loved* Lord Howe and his officers, feasted and feted them interminably. Why, one would have thought it was a holiday season! Such revelry and frolicking! I call it scandalous, General Arnold."

"There are indications that Sir William may be ousted, Mrs. Knox."

"Ah, then the Loyalists will have to sober down," she said.

The camp at Valley Forge resembled a vast city of ramshackle huts, crisscrossed by unpaved lanes. Nothing could disguise its ugliness, not even the greening hills that encircled it, or the fresh spring foliage of the trees. Washington had his headquarters in a stone farmhouse. Above the door floated the blue banner of the commander in chief and the recently adopted flag of the United States, thirteen alternating stripes of red and white, thirteen white stars on a field of blue.

Arnold alighted from the coach and went into the farmhouse. His hostess, Mrs. Washington, was gracious and dignified; and Washington asked anxiously about his wound and his recovery in the Albany hospital.

Washington was requiring that all officers of the Continental Army swear to an oath of allegiance. General Knox administered the oath to Arnold. With Washington as a witness, Arnold pledged himself to acknowledge the United States as a free, independent and sovereign country, whose people owed no allegiance or obedience to King George III of England—a country he would forever support, maintain, defend and serve, with fidelity, to the best of his skill and understanding.

With a firm hand, flourishingly he signed the oath: *Benedict Arnold.*

He went with Washington and Knox to inspect the camp and review the soldiers. He had discarded the crutch, for he was determined to be an invalid no longer; now he walked with a cane, trying not to limp too badly. Once he acted as officer of the day; for twenty-four hours all the responsibility of Valley Forge was his alone. But Washington was making other plans for him.

The British were evacuating Philadelphia, Congress would return there, and a new commander must be named to preserve order in the troubled city. Washington felt that Philadelphia must be governed by an experienced American officer who could somehow comply with the wishes of Congress, yet not offend the inhabitants.

"I have chosen you for this post, General Arnold," he said.

So, on June 19, with Washington's blessing, Arnold was on the way to Philadelphia. His two aides Major David Franks and Major Matthew Clarkson went with him.

Perhaps as he left Valley Forge he was thinking of an incident of his visit, something he hadn't discussed with Washington, or anyone, something rather strange—which a great many people would discuss in the future.

That day when he was in sole charge of the camp, a man named Robert Shewell had come to talk with him, very quietly. Shewell was an American who owned a merchant ship, the *Charming Nancy,* now anchored in the Delaware River. The *Charming Nancy's* cargo of tea, sugar, linens and woolens had been bought in a foreign market; Shewell said these wares were to be delivered to the American army. He asked General Arnold for permission to sail the *Nancy* to some American port, where she could dock and unload.

Arnold thought that what Shewell said might be true; and, if true, what he wished to do was not against the law. More likely, Shewell was lying, for he had been involved before in dishonesty and smuggling. More likely, he would sell the cargo to civilians at a huge profit, which was unlawful.

But Arnold didn't question Shewell too closely. He gave him the permission necessary for sailing and landing. He meant to keep an eye on the *Charming Nancy;* later he would buy a half interest in the cargo and thus share those profits.

He thought it would never be known that he was Shewell's partner. . . . Why should other men make money that he might as well be making himself?

15

PROBLEMS—AND PEGGY

WHEN ARNOLD REACHED PHILADELPHIA, HE FOUND THE CITY dreary, soiled, littered with the trash of the British retreat. Detesting untidiness, he ordered that the streets be cleaned, houses and fences mended. Some of Lord Howe's stores and equipment had been left behind; Arnold seized them as public property. He also seized the possessions of Loyalists who had gone to live elsewhere for the war's duration. He said he would hold these things until their owners could prove a right to them—but until that was done, the American army (which he represented) could buy any part or all of the goods for the army's use. To prevent the removal, transfer or sale of such goods, he proclaimed martial law in Philadelphia and ordered all the shops to close until further notice.

The measures were extreme and made him instantly unpopular.

Already the citizens were being governed by the Pennsylvania Council and by Congress. Now it seemed they were to have a military governor, too, ruling with an iron hand. They were disturbed and puzzled.

They did not know—and Arnold did not tell them—that while the shops were closed, he entered into a contract with James Mease, clothier general to the army, to buy up with the army's money quantities of goods which the troops could not possibly have used, but which could be hauled out of the city and sold—for the benefit of Mease and Arnold. By these transactions, Mease and Arnold obtained at the very lowest price much merchandise that was then sold at the very highest price.

Since it was all a secret, no one suspected the new commander. But when he proceeded to establish himself in the finest house on fashionable Front Street, the house in which

Sir William Howe had lived so extravagantly, a few people whispered about him. He had purchased a very expensive coach, and he was employing a coachman, footmen, a butler and valet, whom he attired in livery.

Would it turn out that General Arnold, the American, was just like Sir William, the titled and autocratic Britisher?

The patriot people of Philadelphia, many of them Quakers, had bitter memories of Howe and the social whirl which had surrounded him. The Mischianza pageant was the thorniest of these memories—the Mischianza, that colorful and wildly lavish entertainment staged by the merriest and most imaginative of Howe's elegant young officers!

For the Mischianza the residence and park of Joseph Wharton had been taken over; nothing less would have done, nothing else was large enough. Hundreds of guests attended, but there were twenty-eight central figures. They were the ones who enacted the pageant. Fourteen British officers, calling themselves knights, though they were dressed in silks and satins, ribbons and velvet, with tin-foil shields and make-believe lances. Fourteen young girls, members of leading Loyalist families, wearing Turkish costumes, flowing trousers, veils and turbans, like ladies of a sultan's harem.

In a tournament the knights had tilted and jousted for the favors of the ladies, a lace kerchief or a nosegay of flowers. Indeed, flowers were everywhere in profusion, flowers and music. Afterward there was a magnificent ball, followed by a bountiful supper of most delicious food, then more dancing which lasted till dawn.

Major John André had designed the scenery and costumes for the pageant. Major André was handsome, something of an artist; he scribbled poetry, too. As a Knight of the Blended Rose, in lace, black satin and rose-pink velvet, he was the very picture of a chivalrous young nobleman. Major André had been Sir William Howe's aide; now he was on the staff of Sir Henry Clinton in New York. It was said that more than one pretty Philadelphia maiden pined for him

No, the Mischianza was not forgotten. Or forgiven, either. Why, the girls' Turkish trappings alone had cost upward of twenty thousand dollars. No telling what was the total cost of the orgy. And in wartime! Oh, it was wicked, wicked.

Philadelphia observed the Fourth of July with a "grand festival" at the City Tavern. By comparison with Lord Howe's celebrations, this one wasn't grand at all; it was rather solemn. General Arnold was there with the French minister Monsieur Gerard, who was his house guest. It was said that Arnold had not much wanted a Frenchman under his roof, but Congress had suggested it and he couldn't refuse. He seemed to treat Monsieur Gerard very courteously.

He went to other social events that summer. He seemed to be developing a taste for them—and for the society of Loyalists. He never danced, of course. Looking distinguished, he sat in a chair with his wounded leg stretched out on a stool, while the ladies fluttered admiringly about him.

The whispering increased and spread.

People weren't allowed to travel now, except with a pass issued by the military commander. The Loyalists apparently had plenty of such passes; they came and went, through army lines, to distant towns. But for patriot citizens the passes were few and far between. Was this General Arnold's idea of justice?

And where did he get his money? Surely he spent more in a month than his salary amounted to in a year!

If Arnold had wished to, he could have answered this query simply. He had made other contracts similar to the one with Mease. In New York City and in Newport, Rhode Island, he was trading busily. Sometimes the contracts were lawful; usually they were not—always they were secret.

He never thought of them as a kind of stealing, or of himself as a kind of thief. He would not have indulged the thought for an instant. On the contrary, he would have said that he was merely an investor. And if it was public money he invested for his own profit—what then? Had he ever been sufficiently rewarded by the public? Hadn't he often been cheated and slighted? Here he was, at the age of thirty-seven, battle scarred, permanently lamed! Why shouldn't he pay back into his purse some of the wealth he had lost by his noble sacrifices?

And not all of it was spent on himself. He wrote to Hannah and told her to bring the boys to Philadelphia; he wanted to put them into better and more expensive schools. He was paying also for the education of Dr. Joseph Warren's orphaned children. Dr. Warren, a good and worthy man, had been a friend of Arnold's in Boston. He was killed in the Battle of Bunker Hill. Congress had done nothing for his young son and daughter. They were penniless; no one had come forward to help them. Arnold sent the Warren children a thousand dollars. More than that, he persistently reminded Congress of its neglect until finally the children were properly cared for.

This was a gesture of real generosity. Where children were concerned, Arnold was always generous.

Still, the patriot citizens did not like him—nor did they like his two aides, especially Major Franks. Timothy Matlack, secretary of the Pennsylvania Council, was angry because his soldier son William had been ordered by Franks to fetch him a barber. Matlack said that Franks semed to believe the American soldiers were the servants of their officers. Well, they were not! American soldiers were the sons of freemen; and Matlack said he was thinking of withdrawing William from the army.

Matlack wrote and published in the newspapers some paragraphs which hinted that Franks followed the pattern set by General Arnold, who was haughty and imperious—and perhaps lacking in integrity. To this Arnold replied with a sarcastic comment. Then Matlack wrote more letters, angry and insinuating. Matlack had become an implacable enemy of Arnold's—one of many.

And while the argument with Matlack continued, the *Charming Nancy* bobbed up again. After several delays, Robert Shewell's ship had docked on the New Jersey coast. Shewell notified Arnold that the British threatened to capture and burn the *Nancy*. Promptly Arnold sent twelve wagons belonging to the army to carry back to Philadelphia the cargo, half of which now belonged to him. The tea and sugar, linens, woolens and glass all were sold quietly, and Arnold was that much the richer.

But somehow it was discovered that the wagons, public property, had made a long and mysterious trip for a private errand of General Arnold's.

How queer! The Pennsylvania Council would look into it. The council recalled Major Brown's grievances against General Arnold, and those of James Easton and others. It was even recalled that years ago in New Haven Benedict Arnold had been suspected of smuggling.

Though every day he coped with some new and annoying problem, Arnold was in good spirits—for he had fallen in love with a beautiful girl. Her name was Margaret Shippen. She was eighteen, slim as a willow reed, gay and vivacious, with wide gray eyes and light brown hair. He thought she was the most beautiful girl in the world. Her father was Edward Shippen, a lawyer and a Loyalist.

The Shippens lived in a fine big mansion on Fourth Street; they were a family of wealth and social prominence in Philadelphia. Margaret was the youngest of three attractive sisters. People who knew Peggy Shippen well said that she was spoiled, but clever; she would do anything to get her own way. As a child she'd had tantrums; now it was spells of fainting and hysterics. Yes, Peggy was so strong willed that she could faint whenever she felt like it!

The Shippen girls had been great favorites of Sir William Howe and his staff. The redcoated British officers were constantly in and out of the Fourth Street house. Major John

André was a beau of Miss Peggy's. The artistic major had made a pen-and-ink sketch of Peggy, with her hair powdered and piled high on her head, and wearing a jeweled, beribboned hat he had designed for her. She had wept a little at the departure of Sir William and André and their jovial mates, but soon she dried her tears. Life was too short and sweet for weeping, if nothing could be gained by it.

Arnold met Peggy Shippen at a party in the summer. Then and there, at first sight, he knew she was the girl for him. And from the start she seemed to like this stocky, dark-browed man. She rode with him in his shining coach; he dined at the Shippen home; they were seen everywhere together.

In September he asked Edward Shippen for Peggy's hand in marriage. His fortune was not large, he said, but it was quite ample. He hoped that his private character was above reproach. As for his public character, it was well known.

"And I'm sure, sir, that our differences in political sentiments will be no bar to our happiness."

Mr. Shippen felt rather uncertain about the match. General Arnold was twice Peggy's age, a widower with three children. Whatever his private character, as a public official he was mistrusted by the Pennsylvania Council—and the patriot citizens of Philadelphia were frankly saying that he ought to be in jail.

No, General Arnold was not a son-in-law Mr. Shippen would have selected. But if Peggy was fond of him. . . .

"Has my daughter told you she will marry you, General Arnold?"

"Not yet," he answered. "Nor has she told me that she won't."

"Peggy must decide," Mr. Shippen said. "I shall abide by her decision."

Throughout the autumn and winter Arnold courted Peggy. And the better he got to know her, the surer he was that their difference in political sentiments was slight, after all.

As a Loyalist, Peggy believed that the American colonies should never have separated from England and that, having separated, they could not win the struggle for independence. How could a nation so new and small and poor hope to defeat powerful old England? Four years, nearly five years since the outbreak at Lexington and Concord—how much longer could the rebels go on? Finally they would have to submit again to the mother country. And why not? Wasn't peace more desirable than a vague something called *freedom?*

Recently these same thoughts were running through Arnold's mind. He was bored by a war which kept him on the sidelines, with no chance for excitement, fame or applause. He desperately wanted to get it over with.

Perhaps his hatred of England had always been a personal hatred. He had hated the oppressive taxes, the laws that interfered with his business—not the King, or the fact of being a British subject. He had resented what the British government did to hamper and inconvenience *him,* Benedict Arnold—not anyone else.

Perhaps he had been too impulsive back in 1775. It seemed so. Taxes were even heavier now, trade regulations more abominable. And now all these people like Matlack yapped and snapped at his heels, as vicious as a pack of snarling dogs.

Suppose England did win? That could happen. It was very likely to happen. Well, a man must think of himself, look out for himself!

In the spring it was known that General Arnold would soon have to stand trial for his conduct before a military board. There were numerous charges against him. He was not worried. He told Peggy not to worry; not one of the charges could be proved, he said.

But it was a nuisance just at this time. Peggy had promised to marry him, and they were planning their wedding.

16

THE WEDDING—AND AFTERWARD

THEY WERE MARRIED APRIL 8 IN THE DRAWING ROOM OF EDWARD Shippen's house; and Peggy, in a gown of stiff white satin, had never looked lovelier. Arnold wore his blue and buff uniform, glittering with gold braid. During the ceremony he leaned on the arm of Major Franks; at the reception which followed, he sat on a sofa, smiling and proud, with Peggy beside him.

The wedding guests were mostly relatives and friends of the bride's—though Hannah and the Arnold boys were there. Arnold did not have many friends in Philadelphia—for that matter, anywhere. Some men have the habit or the knack of collecting friends; Arnold had never bothered much about them. He could have counted his friends on the fingers of one hand: Eleazar Oswald, General Philip Schuyler, two or three others.

And Washington, of course. Washington was "affectionately" his friend.

After the wedding he took Peggy to the new home he had purchased on the Schuylkill River in the outskirts of Philadelphia. This was Mount Pleasant, one of the largest and finest estates in America, a magnificent house surrounded by lawns, gardens and orchards, with half a dozen smaller buildings for servants, horses and carriages.

When Hannah first saw Mount Pleasant she had gasped. "Why, Benedict, it's as big and grand as a castle! It *is* a castle!"

"I want you to live here with Peggy and me," he said. "In any home of mine there'll always be room for you, Hannah."

She shook her head. "I'm an old maid now. I don't like Philadelphia; it's too gay for me. And I'd be lost in this mammoth place. I'll go back to New Haven."

So Hannah went back to New Haven and Henry went with her. The two older boys were sent to a school in Maryland; they also would go to New Haven for their vacations.

Arnold had not told Hannah that Mount Pleasant was bought partly with borrowed money; she would have scolded him for it. There were numerous things he couldn't discuss with her now; she wouldn't have understood them. Hannah's view was always so straight and plain. A thing was either good or bad, right or wrong, in Hannah's eyes.

But somehow he never seemed to have as much money as he needed nowadays. He missed the army salary that he had given up when he resigned his Philadelphia command. His expenses were enormous, and he felt that he couldn't live less extravagantly. He had to borrow money to pay some of his bills. And he could tell Peggy about it. Peggy understood her husband perfectly, agreeing with him in everything.

The date for his trial had not yet been fixed. He had asked for an early date, a quick trial. He wanted to get it over and done with! Every day more people seemed to be turning against him, judging him harshly. Washington was to appoint the court-martial. On May 5, he wrote impatiently to Washington:

"If your Excellency thinks me guilty, for heaven's sake, let me be immediately tried and, if found guilty, executed. I ask only justice."

He knew quite well that he was in no danger of being executed. He believed that he would be cleared of all the charges. But he was angry.

Then, in that same week, he communicated with a man

named Joseph Stansbury. He asked Stansbury to come to see him.

In doing so, he took a first step along a path that could never be retraced. . . .

Joseph Stansbury was English born, but for the last twelve years he had kept a glass and china shop in Philadelphia. His customers were nearly all Loyalists, and once he had been arrested for singing "God Save the King" so loudly in his house that his patriot neighbors reported him. While Sir William Howe occupied the city, Stansbury had written and sung reams of verse predicting the downfall of America, and had never been molested.

Stansbury went to see General Arnold and they talked earnestly behind locked doors. The next day Stansbury went stealthily to New York, where Sir Henry Clinton commanded the British forces of occupation. There he talked with the Reverend Jonathan Odell, a Loyalist who was working for the British.

"I have news of great value for Sir Henry Clinton," Stansbury announced.

"Indeed?" Odell said. "I shall put you in touch with him."

But it was Major John André, Clinton's aide, whom Stansbury met at the British army's headquarters. Major André looked quizzically at Stansbury.

"Haven't we met before, Mr. Stansbury?"

"In the home of Mr. Edward Shippen, sir. Mr. Shippen is one of my customers. You were calling on his pretty daughters."

"Oh, yes," André said. "And why are you here?"

"A high-ranking officer of the American army has delegated me to offer his services to Sir Henry Clinton."

André was startled. "Who is this officer?"

"For the present he wishes to be known to you as Monk."

"Monk?" André said. "The name means something, doesn't it? More than a century ago there was a famous general, George Monk, who changed sides in the midst of a war—changing to the side that seemed most likely to win. That Monk had rich gifts bestowed on him for his treachery. I suppose this Monk believes now that England will win this war?"

"Yes," Stansbury said.

"Well, you can tell him that we'll never quit fighting until we do! And this Monk would like some assurance that for his help a grateful monarch will bestow gifts on him?"

"Win or lose," said Stansbury, "Monk would expect to be properly rewarded. Those are the terms of his bargain."

André was silent a moment. "Is he offering to desert the American army and join ours?"

"If you think it's the way he can best be of service to you."

"I shall consult my chief," André said, "and speak with you again tonight, Mr. Stansbury."

When Clinton was consulted, he exclaimed: "Monk? It's Arnold!"

André smiled. "Peggy Shippen's husband. I think so, sir."

"It must be. Arnold's in all sorts of hot water in Philadelphia. But we mustn't rush too hastily into a bargain with Arnold, for he's a very tricky fellow. He has completely deceived Washington—and lots of other honest folk. Tell Stansbury to arrange for a correspondence with Monk. We'll see what comes of it."

"We don't want him deserting to us, Sir Henry?"

"Oh, no. He'll be valuable only if he can furnish information from within the American army. What a pity he has resigned! We must persuade him to get into active service again."

"A correspondence in code?"

Clinton nodded. "You're ingenious, André. You invent the code."

During the next three weeks, André and the mysterious Monk struck up an interesting correspondence. Their letters were written in the code André had invented—or, sometimes, with invisible ink, the message to be brought out by applying fire or acid to the paper, and marked accordingly, either *F* or *A*. Odell in New York and Stansbury in Philadelphia forwarded them, sending them along by Loyalists who were traveling from one city to the other.

If by accident the letters had been opened and read by these travelers, they would have revealed nothing of their real meaning. To any person who didn't know the code, they would have seemed to be merely innocent comments about the writer's health or business affairs.

André referred to himself as *Mr. Anderson,* but Arnold soon guessed who he was. And Peggy knew, for André suggested that she write to him also. His scheme for this was not very practical. He would write, he said, to Miss Margaret Chew, who had been his partner in the Mischianza tournament. Miss Chew was an intimate friend of Peggy Arnold's. André would ask Miss Chew to reply and to show her letter to Peggy; then Peggy would add a postscript—"something about the Mischianza," he said, "or any other nonsense." Between the lines of her postscript, Peggy was to write a secret message in invisible ink.

Though André wrote to Miss Chew, he had no answer from her, and he heard only indirectly from Peggy. In one of Arnold's letters to him was a single sentence: "Madame Arnold presents her particular compliments."

André smiled as he read that; it was enough to convince him that Peggy was quite aware of all that went on. Perhaps later he would hear more from her.

And the handsome major smiled at what General Arnold gave as his reasons for wishing to change sides in the middle of the war. They were patriotic reasons. Yes, Arnold said, he wanted England to win because the victory would be so good for America. His countrymen would then be English colonists again, happy and prosperous, relieved of their burdens.

"Patriotic!" André said to Sir Henry Clinton. "Does he think he can deceive us, too? Does he think we are blind fools? His motives are purely selfish."

"Certainly," Clinton said. "We're dealing with a traitor. But we shall deal fairly with him, and keep any bargain we make. Therefore, Major André, be most cautious in what you promise."

How was Arnold to be rewarded? In all of his letters, this was the question he stressed. He was courageous, he said, prepared to risk everything, but he must know—without doubt!—that the game was worth the candle.

Mindful of Clinton's instructions, Major André answered cautiously. The British wanted information. Monk would always be rewarded for any information he sent. If, by ability or zeal, Monk should make it possible for the British to defeat the American army in some really big engagement, Monk's reward would be tremendous, exceeding his hopes and dreams.

"Well, *what* information?" Arnold demanded.

André was ready with suggestions. "Tell us the number and location of American troops, the size of ammunition stores and where they are to be found. Tell us the movements of Washington's regiments. Perhaps you can induce other officers to do as you are doing, or to desert. Many of Burgoyne's soldiers are still prisoners of war; see if you cannot get them returned to us."

Arnold's next letter contained some bits of information, none of importance. André replied from a British camp on the Hudson River. Sir Henry Clinton was leading an expedition up the Hudson; he had captured the American forts at Stony Point and Verplancks and would continue northward. This was the old maneuver the British had attempted before: to drive a wedge through New York State, which would split the American resistance in two.

André wrote that Sir Henry advised Arnold to rejoin the

army and accept a command somewhere. Then he could allow himself to be surprised by the British, and cut off from reinforcements. If he could surrender five or six thousand men and their weapons, it would be a splendid accomplishment, and Arnold would be paid a great sum for it. André said that he was willing to meet Arnold in some quiet spot where they could talk and plan at length.

On July 11, Arnold sent a message which he signed with a new name—*Gustavus*. He told André that he had set his price for his services; it was ten thousand pounds, or fifty thousand dollars in American money.

"Fifty thousand dollars?" said Clinton. "The price is too dear for us, Major André. See if he won't come down."

But Arnold would not come down.

Clinton, reading the Gustavus letters, looked thoughtful. "Thus far he has given us only a few facts that we could easily have obtained from other sources. Ask him for an accurate map and description of the fortifications at West Point."

"West Point?" André repeated.

"Yes, Major. It is the key to control of the Hudson River, a stronghold. I should like to have detailed information on West Point, the troops there, the officers, the gunboats which are anchored below the fort—and that chain which the Americans have slung across from shore to shore, beneath the water, to stop any approaching vessels. For such a report I might pay fifty thousand dollars, though I'd rather get it for less."

At the end of July, André wrote to Gustavus about West Point, but without mentioning money at all. Arnold replied that he had no map of this key fortress on the Hudson, and did not know how he could get one. He said he hoped to rejoin the American army shortly; perhaps then he could meet and talk with Major André.

The letter was the last that André received for a long time.

"Has he dropped the project entirely?" Clinton asked.

"It seems so," André said. "Well, I shall write to Mrs. Arnold."

The major's note to Peggy was not in code. It was just a reminder of their former acquaintance. He said that he would be very glad to become useful to her. As she would remember, the Mischianza had made him a complete milliner, and if now she needed any supplies of that sort, he would send them to her—as he wished to be "further employed" in these trifling services.

In November Peggy answered politely, saying that she understood Major André's wish to be further employed and thanked him for it. There was very little else in her letter, but André felt that the way was still open for future communications with General Benedict Arnold.

17

RESULTS OF A TRIAL

WASHINGTON'S ARMY WINTERED THAT YEAR AT MORRISTOWN, New Jersey. It was in Norris' Tavern, near the camp and just before Christmas, that Arnold was tried by the court of American officers whom Washington had appointed.

There were eight charges against him. The more serious ones were the issuing of a pass to the *Charming Nancy* and the use of army wagons to transport her cargo; the unwarranted closing of the Philadelphia shops, and the imposing of menial tasks on enlisted men, like young Matlack, who were the "sons of freemen."

The trial had been postponed many times and Arnold was restless at the delay, though not nervous about the outcome. He went to the tavern clothed in his finest uniform and limping on his cane. He heard the charges and boldly denied that he had ever done anything wrong.

He defended himself by telling the court of all the sacrifices he had made, the hardships he had endured for his country.

"I was one of the first to appear in the field," he said, "and never from that hour to this have I abandoned my duty."

He had brought the letters of praise and appreciation that Washington had written to him, and letters from other people who had admired his military achievements. He read the letters aloud.

Was it probable, he asked the court, that having won such honors, he could sink into a course of conduct equally unworthy of a patriot and a soldier?

"No, no!" he cried. "I have been slandered and abused!"

He spoke eloquently, his face flushed, his eyes glowing. He stumped around the room so that everyone could observe how crippled he was, and yet how brave. His judges listened; their verdict would be given on January 26.

Peggy went with him to Morristown to hear the verdict. Looking youthful and delicate and appealing, she might have melted a heart of stone. She was smiling as the chairman of the court arose. But then her smile faded and she wept into her little lace handkerchief.

The pass for the *Nancy* had been illegal and improper, said the judges; and in the use of the wagons General Arnold was guilty of improper and imprudent action. For these two offenses he would be reprimanded by the commander in chief. The other charges were dimissed.

It was the lightest of penalties, but Arnold was furious.

"Reprimanded?" he shouted. "For *what?*"

Very noisy, black as a thundercloud, he stormed about—until Peggy tearfully led him away.

Back at Mount Pleasant, he brooded and thought of revenge. Oh, he would even the score, all right! Let them wait and see! He thought of Washington, and wondered when and how the reprimand would come. He knew that Washington would be sorry to have to deliver the reprimand, for Washington trusted him. Not for a minute had the commander in chief suspected that last summer, as Monk or Gustavus, Arnold had handed on the army's secrets. No, Arnold had been so clever. Therefore it would be unwise to do anything now that might antagonize him.

I need Washington, he thought. I may want to be clever again.

He needed money, too. He could never shake off that need. Money, money. . . .

In March a baby boy was born to Peggy and Arnold. They named the boy Edward, for Peggy's father. Arnold wrote the news to Washington, who sent him a letter of congratulations and best wishes from himself and Mrs. Washington. Later that month Arnold wrote a longer letter. He said that because of his injured leg, his surgeons thought he should not take a command in the army for some time. But he was eager to be of assistance to his country. Perhaps Washington would want him to command a naval expedition?

When Washington replied that no funds or men were available for a project of the sort, he lapsed into sulky silence.

In April Washington publicly reprimanded him—in language so mild that many Americans were displeased. It was much too mild, they grumbled; it sounded like praise! But Arnold had felt that he might escape even this. Angrily he notified Washington that because of his health, he would be unable to accept any command at all until the autumn.

Then, suddenly, his health seemed to improve. Only a few days after the reprimand, he wrote to his old friend General Philip Schuyler, who was now a member of Congress. He said that he wished to render his country any service in his power. Yes, though he couldn't ride and he walked painfully, he was determined to rejoin the army. Someone had told him that West Point was to have a new commander. He begged Schuyler to recommend him for the post.

Then he wrote to Robert R. Livingston, another New York Congressman, making the same request.

Both Schuyler and Livingston liked Arnold; in spite of everything, they had faith in him. Both men talked with Washington, asking him to consider Arnold for the West Point command.

And then once again Arnold sought out Joseph Stansbury.

Stansbury was jubilant. More furtive messages for British headquarters? Ah, he enjoyed carrying them! It was May, 1780, and the war was going badly for America. Congress was weak, the people had never been poorer, the soldiers were weary. With a good hard push in just the right place, England might topple the whole structure of American resistance over the brink, collapsing it into utter ruin. And that, thought Stansbury, would be a lovely thing to see!

He trotted off to New York to call on Major John André. But André was not there. He had gone with Sir Henry Clinton's regiments to South Carolina, where Clinton had successfully attacked Charleston and captured thousands of American troops. Instead, Stansbury talked with a British captain named Beckwith. He told Beckwith that he represented a *Mr. Moore,* and that Mr. Moore wished to complete a business arrangement with Sir Henry, which had been interrupted almost a year ago.

Captain Beckwith was very obliging. He carefully wrote down everything Stansbury said; these papers he would put in the commanding officer's files. Of course, he would gladly receive any information that Mr. Moore might forward.

"Perhaps, though, Mr. Moore would rather wait for the return of Sir Henry and Major André before going on with a really *large* transaction?" Captain Beckwith said.

"Yes," said Stansbury. "I think it would be best."

While Arnold waited, he industriously gathered choice items of information, which were forwarded to Beckwith, to be saved for Sir Henry. This was not hard to do. Arnold often saw Washington, or wrote to him. Washington was planning a campaign to advance upon New York City, so long occupied by the British. He was reorganizing his forces, shifting his regiments about. Already the Americans had regained several forts on the lower Hudson and were hopeful of making more progress. Washington did not hesitate to confide in Arnold—and all that Arnold learned was immediately relayed to Beckwith.

Arnold was quite positive that he would get the assignment to West Point. Washington had said nothing definite, but he had been impressed by the urgent suggestions of

Schuyler and Robert Livingston. He had told these friends that he sympathized with General Arnold's sufferings and was touched by his stanch devotion to the patriot cause. Washington wanted him to have some post of responsibility and honor, either West Point or some other.

Feeling that the question was as good as settled, Arnold visited West Point in June. He would see it for himself, he thought; then when the time came he could report intelligently to Clinton and André, and bind the bargain.

General Robert Howe was the commander at the fort, but it was known that he would soon be transferred. Though he had been a judge at the court-martial at Morristown, Howe was not prejudiced against Benedict Arnold; he greeted him cordially enough.

With General Howe, Arnold inspected the fortifications, and he was astonished at their crudeness. The barracks and huts looked as if they had been hastily thrown together; the embankments were built of logs and earth.

"Don't underestimate them," Howe said, smiling. "They're more solid than they seem. General Washington was the first person to realize that the Hudson must be guarded at this place. Kosciusko, the Polish engineer, built the defenses and was the first to command here. The ground we stand on is granite ribbed and so high above the river that it can't be approached except from the dock at the water's edge. The hills behind us are gashed with gulleys and dotted with smaller forts and ambuscades. In my opinion, West Point is almost impregnable."

"What's the size of the garrison?" Arnold asked.

"About fifteen hundred men. We expect reinforcements of about as many more."

"And you have guns and cannons?"

"Not all I could wish for. More of those will be sent, too."

"Provisions? Food supplies?"

General Howe glanced somewhat curiously at his visitor;

Arnold was certainly showing an unusual interest. "We have no flour or sugar or meat at the moment. But who has? Well, we're not starving—or complaining, either."

They walked out on the point of land which gives the fort its name, and looked down at the river far below. The Hudson was at its narrowest here, the opposite shore quite close.

"That's Martalaer's Rock you see across from us," Howe said. "As you probably know, Washington originally intended to build the main fort there, but couldn't get suitable materials. All that remains are some crumbling walls and heaps of stone. And the redoubt to which one end of the great chain is fastened."

"The chain? What does it weigh?"

"One hundred and eighty tons. The links were forged at a foundry just twenty-five miles from the Point, hauled by teamsters, then welded together and strung from one bank to the other under the surface of the water. The chain can be wound on a spool; beneath it is a second chain, or boom, of linked and hooked logs."

"I suppose it could be disconnected at Martalaer's Rock or on this side?"

"God forbid it ever will be!" Howe exclaimed.

Arnold nodded. "You think the chain and boom will keep enemy ships from navigating the Hudson to attack the fort?"

"I think it should keep them from *trying*," said Howe. "Don't you?"

Now Clinton and André were again at the New York City headquarters. Arnold sent on his detailed knowledge of West Point.

"I shall have the command," he said. And again he set a price for his "co-operation," by which the fort and garrison should fall into British possession.

The price had risen; indeed, it had more than doubled

He now thought that at twenty thousand pounds, his co-operation was cheaply offered. In addition he must have a guarantee that his family and his property would be protected, and that later he would be paid a yearly amount by the British government.

Clinton was slow to answer; and when he answered, he was vague.

During the month of July Arnold, as Mr. Moore, wrote repeatedly—feverishly; Clinton seemed very deliberate and cool. But Arnold would not believe that anything might occur now to shatter his hopes. He was straightening out all his tangled affairs, endeavoring to sell his house in New Haven, turning his belongings into cash, borrowing money—preparing to leave Philadelphia forever. And he continued to besiege Sir Henry with letters.

At last Clinton agreed. For the surrender of West Point, Arnold would be paid what he was demanding. But before that, there would have to be a meeting between Arnold and Major André. With so much at stake, and Arnold's services so costly, a meeting was absolutely necessary. . . .

In New York, Clinton said to André: "You don't object to meeting him, Major?"

"Oh, no. It's all in the day's work."

Clinton frowned. "A fellow of Arnold's stripe is quite beyond my comprehension."

"I've studied his letters," André said. "Any man reveals himself in his letters, at least to some extent. Besides being greedy for wealth, Arnold is immensely vain and falsely proud. He feels that he's never had all the laurels to which he is entitled. The person who criticizes him is an enemy."

"But he is his own worst enemy. You know his wife, Major. What is Mrs. Arnold like?"

"Peggy? Beautiful, luxury loving and ambitious."

"Exactly the wife for him, eh? With a different wife, he might have been a different man. Or perhaps not," Clinton said. "Somewhere, somehow, he's got on the wrong track. Isn't it strange? And frightening? Yes, what Benedict Arnold is, what he has done and will do, is a strange and frightening riddle. He has a sister, I think?"

"So I've heard," André said. "A thoroughly good woman from all accounts."

"How has he managed to pull the wool over his sister's eyes these many years?"

André shrugged. "I wonder. In the same way that he's managing even now, with his commander in chief, I imagine."

"But there's no disputing his military genius, Major," Clinton said. "For it is genius—though not the sort to be trusted."

Something seemed to draw Arnold to the vicinity of West Point. Washington hadn't assigned him to the post. He was chagrined and impatient at having to wait when his own plans had finally been made. He knew that Washington was concentrating his forces on the Hudson and would move them southward for the attack on New York City. On July 31, Arnold went to King's Ferry, where the army was to cross the river. He knew that Washington would supervise the crossing; he meant to have a word with him.

The day was bright and sunny, but with a brisk wind blowing. Arnold found Washington on a ledge of rock above the river's west bank. Tall and erect, Washington was seated astride his horse. He wore a three-cornered black hat and a long black cloak that hung in folds from his broad shoulders. Down at the pier, Colonel Alexander Hamilton and the gallant young Frenchman General Lafayette were directing the loading of the troops on to giant barges. Slowly the barges were poled out to midstream, then to the east bank for unloading.

Washington was surprised to see Arnold.

"What brings you here?" he asked, smiling.

"I've been with friends at the town of Haverstraw, near by," Arnold said. "You're going south to Tappan?"

"Yes, we camp at Tappan this evening," Washington paused. "You may be happy to know, General Arnold, that I have given you a post. I want you to command the left wing of my army in the new campaign—"

Washington paused again, for Arnold was staring at him as if stupefied, with an expression almost tragic.

"What is it?" Washington said gently. "What is it, General Arnold?"

"I—I thought—" He could barely speak; his voice was hoarse as a crow's. "I thought—West Point—"

"But you have always preferred the field—action. As commander of the left wing, you'd have a position of greater honor than at the Point."

"My lameness," Arnold muttered. "My leg."

"Has that not improved? General Schuyler told me that you said so."

"My leg pains me often. I am not fit for duty in the field, sir."

Washington looked perplexed. "Well, then," he said, "I shall assign you to West Point. Come to Tappan tomorrow; Colonel Hamilton will have the commission for you. You must excuse me now, General Arnold. I see that all the ferrying has been done. Good morning to you."

"Good morning," Arnold breathed, and watching Washington spur his horse and ride away, he wiped the cold sweat from his lips and brow.

18

CONSPIRACY

TWO MILES SOUTH OF WEST POINT AND ON THE OPPOSITE shore of the Hudson was a big, rambling white house with a steep roof and a pillared porch facing a stretch of ragged lawn and neglected flower beds. Before the war, this house had been the home of Colonel Beverley Robinson and his family. But Colonel Robinson, a Loyalist, was now an officer in the British army; and Benedict Arnold, the new commander of West Point, would make his headquarters there.

Arnold arrived at Robinson's House on August 5. He had driven from Philadelphia in his coach; with him were Major Franks and Catherine Martin, who had been housekeeper for the Arnolds at Mount Pleasant. Following the curving river road, the coach had rounded Donderberg Mountain and Bear Hill, and stopped just at the foot of Sugarloaf Mountain. The coachman jumped down from his box and began to lift out the luggage. The passengers alighted and looked about them at the dark forest crowding toward the lawn from both sides, the dark slopes of Sugarloaf in the rear.

Catherine Martin, a plump and efficient woman in a starched cap, brushed dust from her skirt and shawl.

"Gloomy, sir," she said to General Arnold. "Gloomy. Not half so nice as Mount Pleasant, is it? The mistress won't like it half so well, will she?"

"We must make it as comfortable for her as we possibly can," Arnold said. "I'm having some of the Mount Pleasant furnishings fetched, rugs and curtains and things. I want you to scour and scrub and get the rooms in order, Catherine. You can hire extra servants from the village of Buttermilk Falls."

"Yes, sir," Catherine said. "And when is Mistress Arnold coming?"

"In a few weeks."

"She'll bring the baby, sir?"

"Yes, of course," Arnold said. "I shall send Major Franks to escort her."

Hearing this, Major Franks smiled—but said to himself that he hoped Mrs. Arnold would behave calmly on the journey. Occasionally, when General Arnold was busy, Major Franks had been asked to escort the beautiful Peggy to social functions in Philadelphia, and sometimes she puzzled him. For instance, at that dinner party last week:

A gentleman had leaned toward Mrs. Arnold and said, over the centerpiece of flowers, "They tell me, madam, your husband is to take the field with Washington in the next campaign." Shrieking, "The field? Oh, *no!*" she had fainted into Major Franks' arms.

It was all he could do to revive her and get her back to Mount Pleasant; and he had no idea why the remark should have distressed her so. Like most young men, Major Franks was charmed by Peggy Arnold, but he often thought she needed a nurse more than an escort. . . .

Arnold also was thinking of Peggy, as he inspected Robinson's House. Yes, it was gloomy—and lonely, too. And the region roundabout was lonely and wild. There was a kind of feud going on in the hills between two bands of ruffians known as Cowboys and Skinners. The Cowboys were Loyalists from neighboring farms; they stole cattle to sell to the British in New York City. The Skinners claimed to be patriot youths and were out to fight the Cowboys. But really one faction was as bad as the other, thieving and plundering, setting fire to haystacks and accosting travelers on the roads.

Arnold walked from room to room. The library was the

best of them, though it had a musty unaired smell. He opened a window and leaned on the sill.

Colonel Richard Varick was coming to be his secretary. Varick would have his desk here in the library. Both Arnold and Peggy knew him and felt that he would do very well at Robinson's House. A quiet, studious young fellow, Varick had been General Schuyler's military secretary. He wanted to be a lawyer, always had his nose in a book and was not likely to notice anything unusual that might occur.

Unusual occurrences? What would they be? How quickly could this drama be played out? Everything now was at a crucial stage, a dangerous stage.

Arnold tapped his fingers on the window frame, thinking. . . .

He must get to work! The sooner he handed over West Point to Clinton, the better for all concerned. The surrender would surely speed the progress of the war—and might end it at once, abruptly, earning for Benedict Arnold more fame than he had ever known, brilliant and enduring fame.

Perhaps afterward he and Peggy would live in England. Hadn't Clinton said that a yearly pension could be procured for them? Arnold might even be knighted by the King. Then Peggy would be a lady. Lady Arnold!

Dear Peggy, she seemed so childlike and frail, and yet was so resolute. She had been drilled in her part and wouldn't fail it. Whatever happened, in any moment of crisis, Peggy would do and say the correct thing.

Later, in his explanations, Arnold might declare that his hatred of France, the French alliance, had inspired him to change his allegiance. There would be some truth in that. It was not the whole truth, but it mattered.

Turning from the window, he paced the library floor, remembering the day last winter when he had gone to see the Chevalier de la Luzerne, who was on the staff of the French minister to America. He had told Luzerne that he had debts which should be paid; if they weren't paid, he would have to quit the Continental Army, never to fight for America again. Naturally, he said, France—as the ally of the United States and also engaged in the war—would wish to prevent that. Naturally France would be glad to lend him the money to pay his debts.

Luzerne had been surprised, smiled a bit scornfully. He said France did not deal secretly with American generals. "A soldier," he said, "does not take money from one country to fight for another."

Arnold had stalked out of Luzerne's office red with embarrassment and hating France and Frenchmen all the more. . . .

Well, he had many tasks before him. He must find somebody to replace Stansbury as his messenger. In Haverstraw there was a man named Joshua Hett Smith who might help. Smith was a prosperous landowner; his relatives were Loyalists, but no one knew precisely what Smith himself was. Once he had acted as a spy for the Americans, yet he seemed to have connections with the British.

At the time of his visit to West Point in July, Arnold had asked Colonel John Lamb about Mr. Smith. Lamb was Eleazar Oswald's friend; he had marched to Quebec with Arnold and had organized the artillery company for which Arnold had advanced a thousand dollars. At Compo Beach, the Danbury raiders had wounded Lamb; but he was back in service now, an artillery officer on the Hudson.

"Joshua Hett Smith?" Lamb had said. "Have no truck with him, Arnold! Smith hasn't an honest bone in his body. He talks out of both sides of his mouth."

But Lamb was a blunt chap, stalwart in the American cause—and he did not guess why Arnold was inquiring. Arnold thought he would see Smith at the earliest opportunity.

Colonel Richard Varick reached Robinson's House August 13. Catherine Martin had cleaned the library, and for the next two weeks Varick sat at his desk from morning till night copying lists for General Arnold. It seemed that Arnold was making a most thorough survey of West Point, listing the three thousand troops in his command, classifying them as gunners, sharpshooters or foragers, listing the supplies of every sort, especially of ammunition, counting the horses and mules.

Varick could not imagine why General Arnold wanted these lists. "I haven't yet counted the cats and rats that roam the camp," Varick said to Major Franks. "I suppose I'll come to it, though."

Also Varick copied maps of the West Point fortifications and of all the smaller forts in the hills. The chain across the Hudson had been examined—it was not as strong as General Howe had believed; some of the logs in the boom had sunk, some of the iron links were twisted. Arnold did not repair the chain, but he ordered Varick to write a report of it.

Like the lists and the maps, the report was meant for Clinton; at the bottom of the paper, Arnold added something that Varick never saw: "A single heavy ship could break through this chain."

Arnold had called on Joshua Smith in Haverstraw; now Smith was a frequent caller at Robinson's House. He was a fat, pompous little man; Arnold felt sure that he was a Loyalist and that an acquaintance with him would be useful. But as yet Smith had not located a reliable messenger; the days flew by and Arnold was growing anxious.

One morning Arnold told Varick to write out a pass for Mrs. Mary McCarthy, a woman in Haverstraw who wanted to go with her children to New York City.

"I have some letters for Mr. John Anderson, a merchant in New York," Arnold said. "Mrs. McCarthy will deliver the letters for me."

Varick glanced up wonderingly. "Mrs. McCarthy is the wife of a British prisoner of war, sir."

"Well, what of it?"

"If your letters are important, should they be entrusted to her?"

"They are merely business letters, about a stock of merchandise that John Anderson is handling for me. Issue the pass, Colonel Varick."

"Yes, sir," Varick said, and he wrote out the pass for Mrs. McCarthy. At noon he saw the woman being rowed down the river in one of the West Point barges which displayed a flag of truce. Somehow this seemed strange to Varick; he spoke of it to Major Franks.

"I think it's a mistake to let the kinsfolk of Britishers travel freely at such a time, Franks. And another thing, I don't like this Joshua Smith, who's always tugging at Arnold's coattails. I fear Smith is a Loyalist; by associating with him, the General may get into trouble."

Franks nodded. "Smith has all the earmarks. But could you or I advise Arnold against him? I've been five years with Arnold. I've never known him to listen to advice. He's stubborn, thinking of himself as eternally right and everyone else wrong."

"I have believed in him and admired him. But now," Varick said, "somehow I'm worried. I have the feeling that a cloud hangs over us here, a feeling of tension. Arnold is constantly irritable, strained. Why? What's in his mind? He's neglecting his duties at the Point to compile these interminable lists. He seems to be rushing, plunging toward some hidden objective—and what can it be?"

"I don't know," Franks said. "But you may be sure that he'll cheer up when Mrs. Arnold comes. He's been roaring like a lion—he'll soon coo like a dove. I leave for Philadelphia tomorrow to fetch her."

"Is the trip to be made by coach?"

Franks smiled. "By coach and by wagon; the one for rainy weather, the other for sun. Both vehicles padded with silk cushions, because of the bumpy roads. The party will be quite large, including a sergeant, a squad of infantrymen as guards, Mrs. Arnold's maid, a woman to tend the baby. We'll be six days on the way, stopping each night in some pleasant spot, where the General has arranged for accommodations, and we'll have hampers of fine foods and wines to regale us. Oh, I have my instructions, Varick, plenty of them. Peggy is the General's greatest treasure; she must be spared any fatigue or inconvenience."

In the towns below West Point and as far south as Dobbs Ferry, there were outposts held by American cavalry. Arnold sent orders to Colonel Elisha Sheldon at Salem and to Major Benjamin Tallmadge at North Castle that he was expecting communications from Mr. John Anderson, a "mercantile gentleman." Any letters Mr. Anderson might address to him must be brought immediately to his headquarters. If Mr. Anderson should ever appear in person, he must be passed through the American lines.

Colonel Sheldon was a gruff, strict officer. He didn't much fancy passing a civilian, mercantile gentleman or otherwise, throug the Salem camp. But when a letter came from Mr. Anderson, he forwarded it to West Point.

Arnold was elated—for not until then was he sure that Mrs. Mary McCarthy had been able to reach Major André in New York.

Now the meeting that Sir Henry Clinton insisted upon could be planned.

A British armed sloop, the *Vulture,* was stationed in the Hudson. Arnold knew that Colonel Beverley Robinson was on the sloop. He suggested that André board the sloop and that the *Vulture* then sail to Dobbs Ferry. If Robinson and André disembarked there, Arnold would be waiting for them. Robinson was to have a flag of truce; if challenged by an American sentry, he must say that he was going up the river to his house, to get some of his belongings. André, as Mr. Anderson, wouldn't have to say anything at all.

Early in the morning of September 11, Arnold in his barge was rowed downstream by eight oarsmen. He did not have a flag of truce tacked on the barge—afterward he was sorry, for some small gunboats were guarding the *Vulture.* When the barge was sighted, one of the gunboats fired, a shower of lead peppered and hissed in the water.

Arnold had not dreamed that this might happen.

"Make for the shore!" he shouted to his men. "Into that cove!"

Like a big unwieldy whale the barge wallowed and swerved toward the river's west bank, with the little gunboat in pursuit.

Amazed and irate, Arnold got out and climbed to the shelter of a tree-covered bluff, where he waited several hours for André and Robinson—not knowing that on the east bank they waited for him.

Well, he would have to try again. In a raging temper he returned to West Point. But perhaps he had been seen by someone who would mention it to Washington? He must mention it first!

"I was at Dobbs Ferry today," he wrote that evening to the commander in chief. "I went to establish signals and to have a beacon fixed on the mountain, so that in case the enemy comes up the river, the countryside can be alarmed."

19

THE PLOTTERS

ON THURSDAY, SEPTEMBER 14, PEGGY WITH HER GUARDS AND servants, like a royal procession, arrived at Haverstraw. Arnold met her there, going down the river in his barge, which was decorated with flowers and banners for the joyful occasion. Glowing with excitement and pleasure, he clasped his wife in his arms and exclaimed over his infant son. Peggy was looking pale, but she said the trip had not been too hard. Major Franks had been most attentive, and they were not bothered by the prowling Cowboys and Skinners.

The Arnolds stayed that night as guests in the home of Mr. Joshua Hett Smith. After supper the General and Peggy talked for a long time in private, then Arnold conferred with Mr. Smith.

He saw now exactly how Smith could be fitted into his plans, but he still was not sure how far to trust him. In their conversation, he told Smith only enough to keep him interested and willing to help.

On Friday Arnold took Peggy and the baby to Robinson's House. Colonel Varick was at the dock with four soldiers, who bore on their shoulders a feather bed stretched between poles. This was by Arnold's orders; he did not want Peggy to have to toil up the steps that mounted from the dock to the lawn. Very tenderly he lifted her to the feather bed, and the soldiers carried her clear into the house and up to her chamber.

While Peggy rested, Arnold was in the library writing to André. Now he set the date for their face-to-face encounter that Sir Henry Clinton thought so necessary. He wrote in code, and definitely—there must be no more slips or misunderstandings!

"I will send a person by water to Dobbs Ferry on Wednesday, the 20th, between eleven and twelve o'clock at night, who will conduct you to a place of safety. You must be disguised. If I do not hear from you before, you may depend upon the person's being punctual."

As he folded and sealed the paper, Colonel Varick came into the room.

"I did not call you, Varick," Arnold said.

"Excuse me, sir. A note from General Washington."

The note was important; Arnold saw that at a glance. Washington said that Sunday evening, September 17, he would cross the Hudson at King's Ferry and spend the night at Peekskill, on his way to Hartford. He asked Arnold to send fifty men to Peekskill, for he was traveling without a guard.

"Say nothing of this to anyone," Washington cautioned. "I want my journey to be secret."

Well, here was a choice morsel for Sir Henry Clinton! Until the men from West Point reached him, Washington would be accompanied by just a handful of his officers at the ferry. How easily he could be captured there!

Arnold got a fresh sheet of paper, dipped his pen into the ink again. Dismissing Varick curtly he dashed off a second letter to André, containing this news. He addressed both letters to Mr. John Anderson, then summoned Varick.

"These go to Colonel Sheldon at North Castle," he said. "Give them to a courier."

Varick went out to find a courier.

More letters for Mr. Anderson? Varick frowned. Who was Mr. Anderson, and why did General Arnold write to him so often?

Mr. Joshua Smith and his wife were at Robinson's House for the week end. On Sunday Arnold invited Colonel John

Lamb and some other officers from the fort to dinner at noon. Major Franks and Colonel Varick were present, and Catherine Martin had prepared a splendid meal.

But the dinner was not a success, and Arnold felt that his aides were largely to blame. Colonel Varick was openly hostile toward Mr. Smith. Major Franks, usually polite and genial, seemed depressed and nervous. What had got into these two young men? Arnold was ashamed of them.

Colonel Lamb was at fault, too. Scarcely were they all seated at the table than Colonel Lamb was speaking out in his loud, forthright fashion. Yesterday Arnold had sent several hundred soldiers away from the fort to chop firewood in the hills, and had dispatched as many more on other errands. This was unwise, Colonel Lamb said; it weakened the garrison. Suppose the British should attack suddenly? It was rumored that the neighborhood bristled with spies.

"In my opinion, Colonel Lamb," Varick said—and he gazed straight at Mr. Smith—"in my opinion Loyalists are a greater menace than British spies."

Arnold listened in angry silence. How did Lamb dare to question any ruling of his superior officer? How did Varick dare to voice an opinion? Or to *have* an opinion? And why should Major Franks seem nervous? It was Arnold himself who should be nervous. And he was, he was! Only with effort could he conceal his reaction to the stupid chattering.

There was an interruption then, though not a happy one. With the dessert of pudding and fruit, a serving-maid brought Arnold a letter which had just been delivered at the front door. He scanned it quickly. It was from Beverley Robinson, informing him in veiled language that Major André, as John Anderson, would keep the appointment for next Wednesday night, but would be aboard the *Vulture,* near Tellers Point. So Arnold's plan must be slightly altered—

He looked up and saw that everyone's eyes were upon

him. Pocketing the letter, he said casually: "Colonel Robinson desires an interview with me."

"An interview? Well, don't grant it!" Lamb said. "Beverley Robinson? One of those Loyalists Varick so aptly condemns. What can he have to tell you, sir?"

"He wishes to consult me about some of his belongings stored in the house."

"Let him write you about it. An interview might be regarded as a favor, a gesture of friendliness. Ask General Washington what he thinks next time you see him."

Arnold smiled grimly. "I will, Colonel Lamb. I will."

When the awkward meal was over, he beckoned his aides aside.

"Major Franks, you and I are riding to Peekskill within the hour to greet General Washington. Colonel Varick, I leave things here in your care. And I warn you, there must be no lack of courtesy to the Smiths!"

"Yes, sir," Varick said.

Arnold and Franks returned from Peekskill Monday morning. No attempt had been made to capture Washington; Arnold thought Sir Henry Clinton must have a reason for holding off. Or perhaps Clinton had not received the news in time. That, of course, was always a problem; messages could go astray, get lost—or be intercepted. That was why Arnold was eager to conclude this whole business. The suspense annoyed him. That was why he must let Robinson know that he understood André's change of plan.

And Washington had provided him with the opportunity.

"Your Excellency, do you wish me to reject Colonel Robinson's proposal for an interview?" Arnold had asked at Peekskill.

"Yes," Washington said. "Write and tell him that this is no concern of yours."

Washington then inquired about Peggy Arnold and the baby. "I should like a glimpse of your lovely wife and little boy. May I stop at Robinson's House on my way back from Hartford? Saturday, perhaps, or Sunday?"

"Please do," Arnold said. "Mrs. Arnold will be delighted. You honor us."

As soon as he reached home, he called Varick into the library. "I'll reply now to Colonel Robinson," he said. "Take my dictation, Colonel, and send the letter off."

Pacing the hearthrug, he began to dictate. But Varick laid down his pen.

"Sir, I do not approve of this reply. It has too warm a tone."

Arnold swung around, glaring. "What?"

"Robinson is an enemy to our country."

"You are presumptuous, Colonel Varick."

"I'm thinking of you, sir." Varick blushed miserably, to the roots of his hair. "Your reputation."

"Oh, indeed?" . . . The impudent young puppy! Arnold suppressed an impulse to thrash him, to boot and belabor him. "Well, you write the letter, Varick, one that suits *you*. I'll sign and seal it."

The letter Varick produced was stilted and cold. As Arnold signed it, he slid into the folds a small piece of paper on which he had scribbled in code. This was the real message; it confirmed the date for the meeting with André and told Clinton of Washington's further movements.

He sealed the letter with a splash of red wax.

"I'm sorry, sir," Varick mumbled, "to have seemed unmannerly—"

"Don't apologize," he said; and when Varick was out of the room, he muttered: "No, don't waste your breath, my lad, for I'll not have to put up with you much longer."

Later that day, Mr. Smith came. Arnold walked with him in the yard, where there were no eavesdroppers.

"You'll not go to Dobbs Ferry," Arnold said. "Mr. Anderson is to sail up the river to Tellers Point."

"On the *Vulture?*" Mr. Smith did not know who John

Anderson was; he knew only that Anderson's mission was somehow advantageous to the Loyalist cause, and that it was mysterious. Mr. Smith liked mysteries. He rubbed his hands and said: "I shall fetch him to you from the sloop."

"You'll take Mr. Anderson to your house in Haverstraw. I'll talk with him Thursday morning."

Mr. Smith grinned slyly. "Have no fear of being disturbed. My wife and family are already at the village of Fishkill visiting relatives."

"Here is your pass. It reads, 'Permission is given to Joshua Smith, Esquire, a gentleman Mr. John Anderson who is with him, and his two servants to pass and repass the guards near King's Ferry at all times.' You said, didn't you, that you could get a boat?"

"Oh, yes. From the Cahoon brothers, and they'll row me to the sloop. The Cahoons are tenants of mine."

"Then I think that's everything," said Arnold.

In New York City, Sir Henry Clinton was talking with Major André. Clinton was fond of André; he had a fatherly feeling for him.

"Don't go behind their lines, Major."

"No, sir."

"And don't wear a disguise."

"No, sir."

"If you should be caught behind the American lines, and in disguise, you would be adjudged a spy; your fate would be that of a spy. Remember, you are not a spy."

"I'll remember, sir."

"Beverley Robinson knows little about this," Clinton said, "and Sutherland, the *Vulture's* captain, even less. Don't tell them more than you have to. I hope Arnold has the sense to keep his mouth shut, too."

"I believe he will. I believe it will all go smoothly." André smiled. "Well, good-by, Sir Henry. I shall report to you Thursday evening."

They shook hands.

"Good-by," Clinton said. "And the best of luck!"

At seven o'clock Wednesday evening, September 20, André boarded the *Vulture,* which was anchored off Tellers Point, fourteen miles below Arnold's headquarters. Colonel Robinson and Captain Sutherland welcomed him.

Sutherland said that during the day a white flag had been raised from the rocks ashore. "Robinson thought it might be General Arnold wanting to communicate with him. I sent out a boat—and the rogues, whoever they were, fired on it!"

"Probably some prank of the Cowboys," Robinson commented.

"I shall protest to Arnold, anyway," Sutherland said. "He knows we're here, and under a flag of truce."

At eleven o'clock Major André went on deck to await the person Arnold was to send to the *Vulture.*

He waited and watched until midnight, until sunrise. But nobody appeared.

20

DARK HOURS

THURSDAY MORNING ARNOLD WAS WAKENED BY A KNOCKING on his bedroom door. Colonel Varick was in the hall.

"A farmer named Samuel Cahoon has just left this note, sir," Varick said.

Cahoon? That was Smith's tenant. Probably Smith was writing to say that André was hidden in his house at Haverstraw.

Arnold took the note, shutting the door on Varick. The note was short; as Arnold read it, his heart sank. Smith had been unable to get a boat from the Cahoon brothers. He had argued with them until long after midnight; they would not budge. The most Smith could accomplish was to persuade Samuel to ride to Robinson's House to tell Arnold of his failure.

Arnold threw on his clothes. Now Peggy was up, asking her husband what had happened, whether this meant that the whole elaborate scheme had fallen through.

"I don't know," he said. "I shall see. Smith is a fool. The

Cahoon brothers wouldn't obey him. I could have made them obey me. If the *Vulture* is still at Tellers Point, and André still on it, there is still hope."

He kissed Peggy and hastened downstairs, shouting to Varick to order his barge. In a very few minutes he was speeding down the Hudson.

At a place above Tellers Point he stopped and peered through his telescope. Yes, he could see the British sloop; it had not moved. But was André aboard it? That was the uncertainty. Nothing more could be done until he knew.

He went back to Robinson's House, where he received a strange letter.

It was Captain Sutherland's protest against the Americans who had fired on the *Vulture's* dory; but it was signed, "John Anderson, Secretary," and the handwriting was André's.

Arnold breathed a sigh of relief. So André was on the sloop!

Tonight, Arnold thought. I'll meet him tonight. . . . Gathering up all the lists and maps Varick had copied—and several lengthy documents he himself had written, that Varick had never seen—he folded them into a neat packet and set out for King's Ferry, where he ordered the American quartermaster to deliver one of the army's boats to Joshua Smith's landing at Haverstraw.

That Thursday evening in an upper room of Smith's house, he spoke to Mr. Smith's tenant, Samuel Cahoon. "You and your brother Joseph will make a little excursion for me tonight, Samuel," he said.

Samuel was a brawny, slow-witted man, as black browed as General Arnold.

"No, sir. We were up all of last night. We have to get our sleep."

"You're not a Loyalist, are you?"

"No, sir!" Samuel said emphatically. "A pesky varmint of a Loyalist? No, sir!"

"Then you'll want to serve your country. This excursion is for the benefit of the American cause.

Samuel shuffled his big feet. "What is it you aim for us to do?"

"Nothing in the least difficult. You must row Mr. Smith to the *Vulture* off Tellers Point. I have the boat; all you and Joseph need do is ply the oars. A friend of Mr. Smith's and mine is on the sloop. You'll row him ashore near Long Clove Mountain. It's only six miles—"

"And be shot at by them dratted British gunboats on the river? Oh, no!" Samuel said. "No, sir!"

Arnold stepped to the window and motioned to Smith, who was in the yard talking with Joseph Cahoon. "Bring Joseph up, Mr. Smith."

Joseph was so like his brother that they might have been twins. When both men were before him, Arnold said: "Now you chaps are going to do this, and you may as well be sensible about it. If you aren't, I shall brand you far and wide as working for the British."

Samuel shook his head. "We've no mind to, General Arnold. We won't."

"I'll give you each fifty pounds of flour. How's that? I'll wager you haven't had an ounce of good wheat flour for more than a year."

"No, we haven't," Samuel said. "Patriots don't eat good flour in wartime. We've sent our crops to the army. But just the same—"

Arnold's patience was wearing thin. He pounded his fist on the table. "You'll do as I order or I'll have you arrested and flung into jail! Do you hear me? Jail!"

Samuel looked at Joseph, a sad, frightened look, and Joseph nodded.

"I reckon we better," Samuel said.

The night was beautiful. Arnold went on horseback down

the river road to a spot opposite the *Vulture's* moorings. Behind him, on another horse, trotted a servant of Smith's; the servant was leading a third horse that had no rider. Arnold dismounted and told the servant to go a little distance away and wait there. It was twelve o'clock; the river was smooth and tranquil.

Arnold crouched in the bushes, tense and expectant. He knew that Smith had started much earlier. He had written a new pass for Smith and had given him also a very small scrap of paper, on which was penned: *Gustavus to Anderson.* This was to assure André that Smith was acting for Arnold and could be relied upon. As a matter of fact, Arnold had been disgusted with Joshua Hett Smith for last night's blundering, but he could not cast him aside now. He had no one else to help him, and the great moment for which he had planned so long was here, at hand.

Straining to hear, he caught the sound of rippling water, merely a whisper of sound, for the Cahoon brothers had muffled their oars with sheepskins. Then the boat snubbed the sandy shore and Smith got out, followed by a slim young man in an enveloping dark cloak.

"Gustavus," Arnold murmured.

"Anderson," murmured the young man.

While Smith perched himself on a rock and the Cahoons remained in the boat, Arnold and the young man withdrew to the shelter of a cluster of fir trees on the high bank.

They talked then of many things—the reward, which to Arnold was the most important thing, when he would be paid and the promise that his family would be protected; the details of the surrender of West Point. Arnold gave André the precious packet of papers; they were the proof that he had kept his part of the bargain with Clinton. He said that when the fort was attacked, he would make a show of resistance; it would be just pretense. Afterward, he would join the British forces. He thought that his example, his influence as a foremost American officer, would bring many thousands of dissatisfied Americans into the British army.

Gustavus and Anderson were deep in conversation when Smith approached. It was four o'clock, Smith said. The sky in the east was streaked with pink; it would soon be dawn—and the Cahoons were grumbling.

They went with Smith to the boat.

"Row Mr. Anderson to the *Vulture,* Samuel," Arnold said. "And hurry!"

Samuel looked up defiantly. "No, sir. Joseph and I, we won't—and that I swear. We've had enough of your carryings-on. We're going home."

Arnold was in a fury. He stormed, ordered, commanded. It was no use. The Cahoons would row as far as Smith's landing, not the six miles to the sloop.

"You have an extra horse, General," Smith said. "I was to have ridden it. Why not allow Mr. Anderson to ride the horse to my house? It will be a snug haven for him. I'll come with the Cahoons in the boat."

"Your house? Well, I can't think of any other place." Arnold frowned. "What do you say, Mr. Anderson?"

The young man glanced about him. "I believe that I am behind the American lines, am I not?"

"Yes, sir."

"Then let us ride to Mr. Smith's house without delay. I came in the dark, I shall go in the dark. Whether one night or the next is now of little consequence—for, as I see it, there is no turning back."

It was full daylight when Arnold and André reached Smith's house. Smith had not yet arrived. Arnold had a key; he unlocked the door and led André to the upper room. André tossed off his cloak and stood forth in his scarlet uniform and burnished boots.

"You're not disguised," Arnold said.

"No, General. I am not a spy." André paused, his handsome head tilted. "What's that terrific noise? An explosion!"

"Cannon fire!" Arnold rushed to the window; he grabbed his telescope from his belt and leveled it. "Cannon fire at Tellers Point!"

"Do you think," André said, looking over Arnold's shoulder, "that your people may be bombarding the *Vulture?*"

"If so, it's not by my orders! And it cannot amount to anything. A random shot or two. Sit down, sir, and rest. You must be tired."

Smiling, André sat down. But the noise continued, and soon Mr. Smith was running up the stairs, panting.

"An attack on the *Vulture!*" Smith gasped. "The sloop has weighed anchor, she's dropping downstream."

"Ah, a complication, isn't it?" André said. "How will I get back to New York, General Arnold? Perhaps Mr. Smith can find a more obliging pair of oarsmen."

"You must go by the roads," Smith said. "I'll escort you. We'll cross the river and ride southward—"

"Isn't that rather dangerous, Mr. Smith? Not for you or for General Arnold. For me?"

"Mr. Smith has passes," Arnold said, "if you should be challenged, though I think you won't be. I shall write a pass for you, also, a personal pass. I suggest that you put the packet of documents inside your stockings."

"Inside my stockings? Why, I should never have thought of that! How clever you are!"

"And you must borrow some garments from Mr. Smith."

"Would they fit me, General Arnold? Too large, I fear. Thank you, I shall travel in my own garments."

"I've a beaver hat would fit you," Smith said. "And a purple coat trimmed in gold lace. Leave off your uniform jacket and if the coat's too large, wrap it around you—"

"Oh, very well." André's smile was tinged with sarcasm; he shrugged. "I suppose a man in my situation cannot afford to be critical. Shall we go immediately? Somehow I begin to feel anxious."

They did not go immediately. By noon Arnold was back at Robinson's House, assuring Peggy that they had no reason to worry, the plan had succeeded. But it was late afternoon when Smith and André galloped out of Haverstraw, dusk when their horses clattered onto the ferry to cross the river. At nine o'clock an American militiaman halted them and demanded to see their passes.

"Joshua Hett Smith and John Anderson, a merchant? General Arnold's signature, eh? All right," the militiaman said.

"We're bound for White Plains," Smith said. "What's the best route?"

"By way of North Castle. But don't try it tonight," the militiaman answered. "Those tricky Cowboys are abroad. There's a farmer lives near by. Stay with him and go on in the morning."

"You're not thinking of taking the sentry's advice, Mr. Smith?" André said, as they spurred their horses.

"Oh, yes," Smith said. "It's a warning. We must heed it, or the fellow might report us."

So they slept in the farmhouse. Early Saturday morning they were on the road again. They went six miles, then Smith stopped.

"Now, Mr. Anderson, you may proceed alone. I must return to Haverstraw."

André was astonished. "What! Alone? I do not know this region. And General Arnold wishes you to accompany me."

"You'll be perfectly safe, sir. No risk at all. It's possible you may meet some of our Cowboys and they may plague you a bit. But they're stanch Loyalists and quite harmless."

"Ah, I'm glad of that. You're positive the Cowboys *are* Loyalists?"

"Positive! British sympathizers. Well, good day to you, Mr. Anderson."

"Yes, indeed," André replied. "Good day to you, Mr. Smith."

He rode on, through the village of Chappaqua. At Pleasantville he saw a small boy pumping water from a cistern. He reined in.

"Am I bound for White Plains, lad?"

"Yes, sir. But the Cowboys are skirmishing ahead. I'd say, branch off here to the Tarrytown pike."

The Cowboys, the tricky but harmless Loyalists, all British sympathizers? André veered toward the Tarrytown pike, cantered a mile, over a bridge—

Three burly, unshaven youths swarmed up from under the bridge. They had muskets in their hands; they snatched at André's bridle.

"Get down, traveler! Fast, now. Get down!"

He leaped from the saddle. "You may lower your guns, gentlemen," he said. "The guns are too close to my breast. And I am of your politics."

The three youths stared blankly. One of them asked: "What politics is that?"

"You are Cowboys, aren't you?"

"We're Skinners."

"Skinners?" The word was new to André; it had no meaning for him.

"Patriots. And so you'll be, if you know what's good for you!"

He felt suddenly sick with dread, but he smiled. "Exactly, gentlemen. I'm John Anderson, a patriotic merchant from New York. I've been to see General Arnold at West Point on a patriotic mission. You know General Arnold?"

"O' course we do."

"Well, I have passes from the General." He displayed the passes. At the same time he extracted a gold watch from his vest and dangled it on its heavy gold chain. "I suppose you can read?"

"*I* can read." One of the youths, evidently the leader, seized the passes and slowly spelled them out, syllable by syllable. "They look to be all right," he muttered.

But the other two were gazing at the watch. "Hi, ain't that a crest on the watch? Like the Britishers have?"

"It is!" said the first Skinner. "We'll search him, mates! Into the brush with him and off with his clothes!"

They dragged him behind a clump of hazel bushes and stripped off the purple coat, his nankeen breeches and his boots. They examined the inside of the beaver hat. Nothing, nothing. . . .

"Are you convinced, gentlemen?" André asked.

"Hi, he's still got his stockings on! Pull 'em off!"

They pulled off his stockings; the neat packet of documents fell out. The Skinner who could read plucked it up and broke the seal.

"Why, mates, he's a spy! A British spy! He's stolen the maps o' West Point!"

André laughed, though his throat was dry. "Absurd, absurd! Who are you? What are your names?"

"I'm John Paulding from North Salem," said the reading Skinner. "This un's Isaac Van Wart; t'other's David Williams from Tarrytown."

"Now, Paulding, Van Wart and Williams, I must go on to New York. We won't quarrel about it. Just tell me your price."

"The horse," Paulding said. "Saddle, bridle and all."

"And the watch," said Van Wart.

"And one hundred guineas," said Williams. "One hundred each."

"Agreed, gentlemen." André bowed. "Tell me where to send the money—"

But Paulding had remembered something. "Mates, if he's a spy, we've captured him, and whatever property is on him we get as a prize. Yes, so the law says! Horse, saddle, watch, they're ours, anyhow. He's trying to bribe us!"

"I am a patriot—"

"Maybe," Paulding grunted. "And maybe not. Get your rigging on again. We're taking you to Major Tallmadge at North Castle."

21

FATEFUL MOMENTS

WASHINGTON DID NOT COME TO ROBINSON'S HOUSE THAT SATURday; he had been detained at Hartford. But Mr. and Mrs. Smith came from Haverstraw and were again the Arnolds' guests for dinner.

Mr. Smith was jovial and beaming. He told Arnold that John Anderson had traveled safely through the American lines and must now be at White Plains. Arnold was pleased; and he, too, would have been in good spirits, except that again Major Franks and Colonel Varick behaved rudely at the dinner table.

It started when Peggy scolded the maid for serving the salt fish without butter.

"I'm sorry, ma'am," the maid said, "there's no more butter in the pantry."

"I have some olive oil in the cellar," Arnold said. "I bought it in Philadelphia. Olive oil does very well with salt fish."

He went down into the cellar himself to fetch a small cask of olive oil, which was then poured into a crystal cruet. As the maid handed around the cruet, he remarked: "Olive oil is quite a luxury at present. It sells for eighty dollars a pint in the markets."

"Eighty dollars in American money? That would be about eighty pence in English coin," Mr. Smith said. "The American dollar has so little value."

Arnold nodded, but Colonel Varick spoke out quickly: "Mr. Smith, you sneer at everything American. I do not like it! I resent it!"

And Major Franks chimed in: "Yes, and *I* resent it."

Mr. Smith blinked and wagged his head. "My dear Colonel! My dear Major Franks! I do think you are too sensitive. Is it my language that offends you? I am not a scholar—"

"The question is," said Varick, "are you an American?"

Arnold looked at the sputtering Mr. Smith and then at Varick. "Colonel Varick, you will beg Mr. Smith's pardon!"

"For a question that requires only a simple answer? No, sir."

Mrs. Smith rose, wailing, from her chair. "Oh, we have been insulted!"

"Let us talk of something else," Peggy said; and she did so. But the others were silent, as if they could think of nothing to say.

As soon as possible, Arnold got Varick and Franks into the library.

"Colonel Varick, you deliberately affronted Mr. Smith."

"No, sir. But I wouldn't object to affronting him if I had the chance."

Arnold scowled. "Well, let me tell you, that if I asked the Devil himself to dine with me, the gentlemen of my household would have to be civil to him!"

"The Devil?" Varick said. "I can think of companions even less attractive."

"If you mean Mr. Smith—"

"I do, sir. Joshua Smith is a rascal. If he hadn't been at your table, I'd have pitched the wine bottle at his pompous, fat face; and I shall treat him as I like."

Major Franks interposed. "General Arnold, I believe the Colonel is not mistaken about Smith. I really fear he may be an enemy of America—and therefore your enemy. As your friends, Colonel Varick and I would advise you to be wary of him."

Arnold paused, thinking. He must not antagonize his aides; not yet. He must be calm. "I am always to be advised by my friends," he said. "But remember, Franks—and you, especially, Varick—you can't give me orders. I am your commander. I have as much prudence as either of you, and better judgment. You have provoked and embarrassed me. But it would be folly for us to argue more on this matter! I'll not be visiting Smith's house in the future. I doubt that I'll ever be seen with him—anywhere."

Sunday was also a dismal day. It rained; the Smiths left for home; Major Franks rode off to Newburgh; and Colonel Varick went to bed, complaining of chills and fever. The weather seemed to affect Arnold's leg; he walked stiffly. And he was fretful, thinking uneasily of his plan and what was still to be done.

He supposed that by this time André was in New York; he was eager to hear from him. He wondered when Washington would arrive on his way from Hartford. Probably the commander in chief would be attended by officers of his staff—General Knox, General Lafayette and Colonel Alexander Hamilton. Of course, they must all be entertained at Robinson's House—though he had never felt less like entertaining them! Peggy was not well and the baby had colic. And the *Vulture* had moved up the river again to lie at Tellers Point. Why was that?

Brooding, and hating this interval of waiting, he had no idea of the happenings meanwhile at the American outpost at North Castle. . . .

Major Tallmadge had been absent on scouting duty when Paulding, Van Wart and Williams marched their captive into the North Castle headquarters. Colonel Jameson was temporarily in charge there; and Jameson was neither experienced nor shrewd. The story told by the three Skinners puzzled Jameson. He looked at the packet of papers and at the man who called himself John Anderson. He remembered that General Arnold had been in communication with somebody of that name.

"I'll keep the papers for Tallmadge to see, Mr. Anderson," Jameson said. "I'll write an explanation of your capture, and send you back with it to West Point, under guard."

Mr. Anderson bowed. "Very good, sir."

An hour later Major Tallmadge returned, and Jameson repeated the perplexing story. Tallmadge was astounded.

"And you didn't hold the man? Why, he's a spy!"

"No, no," Jameson said. "A great deal of the writing is plainly Arnold's. I recognized it."

"I don't care a fig about the writing!" Tallmadge cried wildly. "With this much information the British could wreck us! And if Benedict Arnold wrote any of it, he's linked in a traitorous plot. I'll get the documents to Washington at once. And you, Jameson, recapture Anderson—and waste not a minute!"

André and his guard were overtaken at Peekskill and hurried back to North Castle. There André wrote a letter to Washington, in which he confessed everything but Arnold's identity as his conspirator. He added that he was not a spy and had not intended to go within the American lines. He hoped that Washington would bear in mind these two true statements.

Monday morning, as Arnold sat alone at the breakfast table, two young officers came riding at a smart pace to Robinson's House. They were Major McHenry and Captain Shaw; they said that General Washington had spent the night in Fishkill and would arrive shortly, and that Colonel Hamilton would be here even sooner.

Arnold shook hands with McHenry and Shaw. "Will you have breakfast with me, gentlemen?"

"We will," said McHenry. "As you know, it's General

Washington's habit to get us up at crack of dawn. We are starving!"

The young officers seated themselves, just as a courier entered the room with a letter for Arnold. The courier was from North Castle; the letter said that a Mr. John Anderson had been captured and was now lodged in the jail at Salem. It was believed that John Anderson was a British spy, for he had with him papers of information on the West Point defenses—and also passes signed by General Arnold. All these documents had been forwarded to General Washington.

As Arnold read the letter, he seemed to feel the world crashing around him. He got unsteadily to his feet. "Begone!" he said harshly to the courier. "And not a word of this to anyone! Begone!"

Major McHenry saw how pale Arnold looked, all the blood draining from his fierce, hawklike face. "What's wrong, sir?"

"Nothing!" he muttered. "If you will excuse me—"

He went upstairs to Peggy's chamber, went in and locked the door. For a few moments he talked with Peggy, earnestly and low voiced, encouraging and instructing her. Then Major Franks was at the door, knocking.

"General Arnold, Colonel Hamilton has come. And the commander in chief is only a mile away."

"Very well, Franks. Order my horse saddled."

"Your horse, sir?"

"Do as you're told, Major Franks."

"Yes, sir."

When he descended to the hall, he had on his cloak and hat. "I am going to West Point, Franks. Receive General Washington and say to him that I shall return in an hour."

He slammed out of the house. Major Franks saw him mount and gallop down the path toward the dock where his barge was moored.

It was now ten o'clock, cold and misting rain. His eight oarsmen were idling on the dock. Jumping from his horse, he stepped onto the barge and shouted to the men.

"Row me to Tellers Point, the *Vulture!* Put your muscle into it! Pull hard!"

The men pulled hard, the barge moved swiftly. As it came within range of the *Vulture*'s guns, Arnold tied his white handkerchief to the flagstaff. Corporal James Larvey, coxswain of the barge, was watching.

"What's that for, sir?" Larvey asked.

"What's it for?" Arnold laughed. "I'm boarding the sloop, Larvey. I'm joining the British."

"Joining the British, sir?"

"Yes, Larvey. Come along with me, I'll get you a good job."

"I'm damned if I will!" Larvey said. "I don't fight on both sides of a war. Not me!"

Arnold had conquered his feeling of consternation. He was alert and brisk. "You're a fool, Larvey," he retorted.

He boarded the *Vulture* at Teller's Point. Captain Sutherland and Beverley Robinson were on deck.

"Arrest these eight oarsmen," he said. "Make prisoners of them."

"But where is John Anderson?" Captain Sutherland queried. "What became of Anderson?"

"Anderson? Oh," Arnold said, "he also is a prisoner. Yes, he's at Salem, held as a spy."

While Arnold was flying down the Hudson, Major Franks was receiving Washington at Robinson's House.

"We are in some confusion, your Excellency," Franks said. "Mrs. Arnold is ill. Colonel Varick is confined to his room with the ague. And General Arnold was called, quite abruptly, to the fort at West Point—though he will be back very soon."

Washington smiled. "Do not distress yourself, Major

Franks. We'll just have our breakfast and then go over to West Point and meet General Arnold there."

Washington, General Knox, Lafayette and Colonel Hamilton breakfasted together. Then leaving Hamilton in conversation with Major Franks, the others went to the landing and were rowed across the river to the fort.

Colonel Lamb was on duty this morning—and surprised to see the generals.

"And where is General Arnold?" Washington asked.

"He has not been here today," Lamb answered.

Washington was a little disturbed, but he inspected the fortifications. They looked neglected, and he spoke of it to Lamb. For more than seven weeks, Arnold had commanded at West Point, yet the defenses were not strengthened.

"If anything, they've been weakened," Lamb declared, with his customary bluntness. "It's bad policy. We're in bad shape to repel an assault. I don't think we could!"

When Washington recrossed the Hudson, Colonel Hamilton was waiting for him at the landing.

"Messages, sir, from Tallmadge at North Castle," Hamilton said. "A packet of documents taken from the person of a suspected spy, and a letter to you from the spy himself. You should have had them yesterday, but Tallmadge's courier missed our party on the road from Hartford."

"Is General Arnold in the house, Hamilton?"

"No." Hamilton hesitated. "It's been reported to me, perhaps falsely, that he was seen in his barge, hastening down the river toward Tellers Point. That was several hours ago—"

"He must be stopped! Ride south, Hamilton. Stop him!"

"Yes, sir. Do you think—"

"I am afraid, Hamilton."

Washington walked into the house, into the library, where Knox and Lafayette were standing, troubled and silent. The documents were on the desk. Washington read them and the letter signed by Major John André of the British army.

"This is treason," he said. "Treason."

"Not—not Arnold!" Knox exclaimed.

"Arnold." Washington's fine eyes were grave, infinitely sad. "Gentlemen, *whom can we trust now?*"

Upstairs, Peggy Arnold was having hysterics. At about the time that Washington was leaving to inspect the fort, she had begun to weep and sob. Catherine Martin, the maids, the baby's nurse had tried in vain to soothe her. Then Catherine had called for Major Franks. Followed by Colonel Hamilton, Franks ran to help; in the upper corridor they collided with Colonel Varick, who was struggling into a bathrobe and coughing hoarsely.

"Mrs. Arnold must be seriously ill," Varick said. "What can we do?"

"Isn't Dr. Eustis at West Point?" Hamilton asked. "I'll send a soldier for him."

Franks and Varick opened the bedroom door. Mrs. Arnold was walking the floor with the baby in her arms. She wore a lacy nightgown, but her hair had been combed and curled. She looked delicate as a flower and very beautiful.

At sight of them she rushed, shrieking, to Major Franks and clutched his sleeve. "Colonel Varick has ordered my little baby to be killed! Oh, how cruel he is! How cruel everyone is to me, Major Franks!"

Varick was horrified. "Why, madam, I've done no such thing!"

She turned on him. "You have, you have! I know it!"

"Mrs. Arnold, this is madness."

"Oh, how I am persecuted!" she screamed, and fell fainting at Varick's feet.

They got her into bed and revived her. But still she sobbed and moaned. "I have no friends in this house. None! I am alone, alone."

Franks bent over her. "You must not say that, Mrs. Arnold. You have many friends. Varick and I—"

"Colonel Varick wants my baby to be killed!"

"Please control yourself," Franks said. "Your husband will soon come."

"My husband has gone. He has deserted me."

"Oh, no! General Arnold is at the fort."

"General Arnold has gone *forever.* I'll never see him again!"

Franks and Varick exchanged a glance of amazement. Reviewing the course of events they could almost believe it.

The doctor arrived and gave Mrs. Arnold a draught of sleeping medicine and gradually she grew quiet. But later she roused. She had heard Washington's voice below in the library; she insisted that she must tell him something.

Washington went to her bedside and took her hand in his. "Mrs. Arnold?"

"You are not General Washington!"

"Yes," he said. "Surely you know me?"

"You're just another cruel man to torture me, now that I'm friendless and deserted."

"You will not be tortured, Mrs. Arnold."

"Where is my husband? You have spirited him away!" Weeping, she clung to Washington's hand. "My husband has gone from me forever, and I shall be made to suffer for it."

"Oh, no," he said. "Never. You are innocent. I should never permit the innocent to suffer for the sins of the guilty."

She closed her eyes then and seemed to relax.

Washington went down to the group of distracted officers assembled in the hall. "Poor lady," he said. "Poor unhappy lady. We must show her every kindness, every consideration."

At twilight, Colonel Hamilton came back from a long and fruitless chase. At a landing far down the river, he had been hailed by a man who rowed a small boat from the *Vulture* to the shore. The man had a letter which Arnold, on the sloop, had written and addressed to General Washington.

"Here is the letter, sir," Hamilton said. "But the *Vulture* is racing toward New York."

22

THE TRAITOR

ARNOLD'S LETTER TO WASHINGTON WAS NOT AN APOLOGY. NOT at all!

He said that though the world might censure him, he had always loved his country, and this act was only another proof of his love. He asked no favor for himself, and expected none—so often in the past his country had been ungrateful to him! But he sought Washington's protection for Mrs. Arnold, who, he said, was as good and as innocent as an angel and incapable of doing wrong.

"I beg she may be permitted to return to her friends in Philadelphia, or to come to me, as she may choose. I request that the enclosed letter be delivered to Mrs. Arnold, and that she be permitted to write to me."

He also requested that Washington send on to him his clothes and baggage, and ended by saying: "I have the honor to be with great regard and esteem, your Excellency's most obedient humble servant, Benedict Arnold."

In a postscript he added that Colonel Varick and Major Franks, as well as Joshua Smith, Esquire, had been totally ignorant of any transactions of his, and must not be held accountable.

Washington had already decided to give Peggy a pass to Philadelphia, now he assigned Major Franks to be her escort. By Wednesday she seemed quite recovered from her illness, and with the baby, her maids and a military guard was starting on her way. The second night of her journey she spent in the town of Paramus, at the home of Mrs. Theodosia Prevost. Mrs. Prevost had some Loyalist connections, and

Peggy felt that she could speak freely to her. She told Mrs. Prevost how very tired she was of the part she had been playing. She was disgusted with the American cause, she said. She had corresponded with Sir Henry Clinton and his agents. In fact, the idea of surrendering West Point had first been hers, and she had persevered until she got her husband into the plot.

Mrs. Prevost listened with interest and remembered it all, but thought that Peggy was boasting a little: the idea must originally have been Arnold's, and the plot shared equally by husband and wife.

When Washington left Robinson's House he went to Tappan where Major André was held in Mabie's Tavern. André had been a model prisoner, quiet and cheerful, his courage never faltering. From his cell he wrote to Clinton:

> I am perfectly tranquil in my mind and prepared for any fate to which an honest zeal for my King's service may have devoted me. I receive the greatest attenion from his Excellency, General Washington, and from every person in whose care I happen to be placed. . . . With all the warmth of my heart I give you thanks for your profuse kindness to me. And I send you the most earnest wishes for your welfare.

He was concerned about his clothing; it had become very soiled and ragged. With Washington's consent, the officials at Tappan allowed his servant to come from New York with fresh, clean linen and the British uniform of which he was so proud.

Flinging the old garments—and Joshua Smith's hideous purple coat!—into a corner, he bathed, shaved, put on his own scarlet coat, his sashes, his splendid gold-hilted sword, and looked a gentleman again.

But was he a spy? The trial would hinge upon that.

Sir Henry Clinton and Beverly Robinson contended that, in any strict interpretation of the word, André was not a spy. It was at Arnold's invitation that he had gone to their meeting. He had relied upon Arnold and the passes Arnold furnished him. He had never meant to go in disguise behind the American lines.

Arnold, too, was saying that André should not be treated as a spy.

"I sent him a flag of truce," Arnold declared in letters to André's judges. "I gave him passports for his safe return to New York." And Arnold wrote violent threats to Washington, angry warnings that unless André was released there might follow the most horrible scenes of vengeance.

"I call Heaven and earth to witness," Arnold stormed, "that your Excellency will be justly answerable for the torrent of blood that may be spilt in consequence."

The trial itself was brief and simple. The military board wanted to be entirely fair to Major André. Was it true, the judges asked, that he had come ashore from the *Vulture,* under a flag of truce, to meet Arnold on American territory —or had he even supposed that he was doing so?

A flag of truce?

"No," he replied honestly. "It would have been impossible for me to suppose that. Certainly if I had come ashore under a flag of truce, I might have returned under it."

Then, by all the circumstances and all the rules of war, he was a spy. The court condemned him to be executed. The date was fixed for October 1.

At once Clinton attempted to have the verdict set aside. He appealed frantically to Washington for a conference between members of his staff and high-ranking American officers. Washington postponed the execution date to October 2, and sent officers to talk with Clinton's men at Dobbs Ferry. The important matter of the flag of truce was discussed.

"General Arnold," said the British representatives, "vows that André did have a flag of truce."

The Americans said they would rather believe Major André than General Arnold. And one of them said that perhaps Clinton would trade them General Arnold for Major André. This, they knew, would delight Washington and many thousands of Americans.

It might also have delighted Sir Henry Clinton, who was grief-stricken over André's capture. But he could not make the trade. He had promised Arnold complete security in his treachery—and he must keep his promise.

During the morning of October 2, Major André wrote farewell letters to his mother and his sisters in England, and sketched a picture of himself, clad in his regimentals, seated in his cell. At noon Major Tallmadge and the guards unlocked his cell door.

He picked up his hat. "I am ready, gentlemen."

With a firm tread he walked out, but when he saw the gallows in the prison yard, he hesitated. "Am I to be *hanged?*"

Tears of pity were in Tallmadge's eyes. He nodded.

"Hanged as a spy? I had hoped for a soldier's death, a firing squad. Ah, well, it will be but a momentary pang!"

He took two white handkerchiefs and bandaged his own eyes.

"Sir," Tallmadge said, "if you wish to speak now—"

André lifted the handkerchiefs. "I pray you, Major Tallmadge, to bear witness that I meet my fate like a brave man."

The noose was sprung, the crowd around the gallows was utterly silent and sorrowful.

Turning away, Tallmadge muttered: "Thus died, in the bloom of life, the accomplished John André of the royal army, a gallant soldier and the friend of Sir Henry Clinton."

Perhaps Arnold had thought he would be greeted as a hero in New York; if so, he was badly mistaken. The younger British officers, who had been André's companions, despised this traitor in their midst. The older officers shunned him. From Clinton he received a payment of money, all he had bargained for, but very little cordiality.

And Peggy, in Philadelphia, was faring no better. The people there said that her residence in the city was dangerous to the public safety. After six weeks of it, she was ordered to leave. In November, with the baby, she went to New York, where Arnold had rented a house for the winter.

He was busy now issuing statements to the newspapers, telling the "inhabitants of America" why he had joined the British, explaining his odd notions of patriotism, urging them to bring the war to a close by doing as he had done.

But he soon learned that the effect of his treason was to inspire the inhabitants of America with a greater determination to win the war. Shocked and outraged, they were more strongly united than ever before. Nobody praised or admired him; he drew no recruits to Clinton's forces. Instead, he was everywhere denounced and hated.

In New Haven, the citizens made a figure of straw and cloth, Benedict Arnold in effigy; they dragged the figure through the streets, then hanged, then burned it. In Norwich a mob marched to the cemetery and destroyed his father's tombstone, merely because carved upon it was the same name as the traitor's.

Where were his friends, the few friends who had believed in him?

Washington had been the most faithful and forgiving of them—and the one to whom he had been most unfaithful. Washington could not forgive him now. "He wants feeling," Washington said. "He is lost to all sense of honor and shame."

In Philadelphia, Eleazar Oswald wrote sadly to Colonel John Lamb: "Let his name sink as low in infamy, as it was once high in our esteem."

And Hannah? . . . Perhaps more than any other person, Hannah knew the depths to which her brother had fallen.

It was not only that he had betrayed his country: he had betrayed her, his parents, all those who had ever cherished and cared for him. And worse, far worse, he had betrayed himself; and in this had betrayed all goodness, and that image of God which is in every man.

Hannah bowed her face in her hands and wept. "He is insane, insane. . . ."

He was not insane, but arrogant and impatient to be in the field.

Commissioned as a British brigadier general, he commanded troops in Virginia that winter and throughout the spring of 1781. He fought with his usual dash and brilliance —often against the very American companies he formerly had led in battle. In September, 1781, he conducted a savage raid on New London, Connecticut, a town only a short distance from his birthplace, pillaging and plundering, setting fire to stores, shops and dwellings, reducing the town to ashes.

His exploits may have pleased the British officers, yet he was not popular with them. They were suspicious of him—for who could tell whether he might not change sides again? From time to time American soldiers made efforts to capture him; there was a price on his head. In Virginia a Yankee sergeant had nearly snared him; but luck was with him and he got away.

One day, while viewing some Americans seized and imprisoned by the British, he said to a blue-coated captain: "What would be my fate, if *I* should be taken prisoner?"

The captain answered contemptuously: "They would cut off that leg of yours wounded at Quebec and at Saratoga, and bury it with all the honors of war, and then hang the rest of you on a gibbet."

By early autumn of 1781, the Americans had gained the upper hand in this long contest. Heavily reinforced with

French troops and assisted by the French navy, they pressed hard and doggedly on the British. In October, the decisive battle was fought at Yorktown, Virginia. Sharply defeated, Lord Cornwallis, the British commander, surrendered; his men laid down their arms. It was the end of the war—and victory for the brave new United States of America.

On December 15, Lord Cornwallis sailed for England. With him, on the British warship, the *Robuste,* went Benedict Arnold. Soon afterward Peggy sailed on a merchant ship to join her husband in London. Peggy had two babies now, for a second son had been born to her. She traveled in style, with maids and nurses.

Arnold's three older sons stayed in New Haven, to live there with Hannah.

23

SHADOWS

IT COULD NEVER BE SAID THAT ENGLAND WAS NOT GENEROUS TO the Arnolds, or forgot any terms of the secret agreement Sir Henry Clinton had made with them.

Arnold himself was given a large salary as a British officer. In London he had more than one audience with King George. He was a guest at many royal functions and was seen strolling in the public gardens with the King's brother and the Prince of Wales. Peggy was rewarded with a yearly pension of five hundred pounds for having rendered "meritorious service" to the Crown; she was introduced to the Queen, who told the ladies of the court to be attentive to her.

This was not all. A commission in the British army was bestowed on young Benedict Arnold, though he was only twelve and far away in America. Richard and Henry each received similar commissions on their twelfth birthdays. With these commissions went a salary, which would continue as long as the three boys lived. And the children of Arnold's second marriage were not neglected. As the years passed, he and Peggy became the parents of two more sons and a daughter. Each of their five children was given a pension, too.

Then why was it that Arnold was not entirely happy in England?

For one thing, he still did not feel that he had been paid quite enough. What about the property left behind in Connecticut, and Mount Pleasant in Pennsylvania? What about the money he might have earned in the American army? Surely the British government would reimburse him! Or the American Congress? Or *somebody?*

He made extravagant and fantastic claims in every direction; when these were refused, he sulked.

And the English people, he felt, were not as friendly as they should have been, to a man who had risked so much for them. Somehow the Arnolds found very few friends in London. Almost their only companions were those Loyalists who had fled from America to England during the war.

Arnold never talked of his treason; he would not let anyone else mention it to him. But he was interested in a project started soon after the war, to erect a monument to Major John André's memory in Westminster Abbey. He contributed to the memorial fund, and sometimes on Sundays he and Peggy went to the Abbey to look at the monument. Other visitors, observing them as they stood reading the inscription to the heroism of André, wondered at the spectacle.

What thoughts were in Arnold's mind?

Did he envy the reverence shown to André, such reverance as would never be his? Or was he silently reproaching André for having blundered in that elaborate plot of Arnold's devising?

He loved Peggy and his children. They were a close-knit family; perhaps their very loneliness drew them more intimately together. But he was restless and bored. He had nothing to do. He asked for a position with the king's government, but was rejected. Hating inaction, he bought some ships and engaged in trade with the West Indies and Canada.

He established a Canadian headquarters for his business in Saint John, New Brunswick; he spent a winter there. In 1787 he moved his family to Saint John. This might be the place for them.

But no, the Canadians were not friendly, either; and Arnold seemed unable to alter the pattern of his habits or manners. He quarreled often with the townspeople and constantly with his business associates—he said they cheated him, and they accused him of dishonest dealings and involved him in lawsuits. At last his house was mobbed; and his effigy, labeled "Traitor," was burned at his front door.

Traitor? What an example of ingratitude it was, he thought. And would he never escape the horrid title?

Angrily, he took Peggy and the children back to London, but he had not escaped.

One day in 1792, in the English Parliament, the Earl of Lauderdale rose to denounce a political enemy, the Duke of Richmond. Lauderdale branded Richmond as a traitor; he compared him with Benedict Arnold—though Arnold, he said, was worse.

When he heard of the speech, Arnold immediately challenged Lauderdale to a duel. The challenge was accepted; they met on a hot summer morning in a secluded spot just outside London.

They were to fire, both at once, when their seconds signaled. They leveled their pistols, the signal was given. Arnold fired—his shot went wild. Lauderdale did not respond.

"Fire!" Arnold shouted. "Fire—or retract what you said in Parliament!"

Lauderdale would do neither. Arnold was enraged, the seconds argued. Finally Lauderdale admitted that he had not meant to hurt Arnold's pride. Rather grudgingly Arnold said that this statement satisfied him.

With every year his restlessness increased. He voyaged on his merchant ships, roaming the seas. Some of his business enterprises were successful, but more of them failed. Slowly his fortunes were declining.

He was in the West Indies when war broke out between England and France. Excited at the possibility of fighting again, he hurried home to ask for a command.

"Wait," he was told. "Perhaps later."

Three times he applied for an assignment in the field—anything, anywhere! He never got one. England, it seemed, had no further use for his rash courage, his military genius.

The months went by, the seasons, he grew older. In 1800 he was ill of a disease he believed to be incurable. He made his will, beginning it with a bequest to his sister Hannah—how long, long ago he had assured Hannah that he would always take care of her! But he was thoughtful now of all the members of his family, providing as best he could for them all, his children and Peggy, naming Peggy, his "beloved wife," as administrator of his estate.

In June, 1801, he was confined to his bed and knew that he was dying.

"Bring me my American uniform," he ordered; and when they put it into his hands, he said: *"I wish I had never changed it for another."*

BIBLIOGRAPHY

Arnold, Isaac N. *The Life of Benedict Arnold, His Patriotism and His Treason.* Chicago: Jansen, McClurg and Company, 1880.

Bradford, Gamaliel. *Damaged Souls.* Boston and New York: The Houghton Mifflin Company, 1923.

De la Roche, Mazo. *Quebec.* New York: Doubleday, Doran and Company, 1944.

Encyclopaedia Brittanica.

Encyclopedia of American History. Edited by Richard B. Morris. New York: Harper and Brothers, 1953.

Flexner, James Thomas. *The Traitor and the Spy.* New York: Harcourt, Brace and Company, 1953.

Lossing, B. J. *Pictorial Field Book of the Revolution.* New York: Harper and Brothers, 1860.

Sellers, Charles Coleman. *Benedict Arnold, the Proud Warrior.* New York: Minton, Balch and Company, 1930.

Sullivan, Edward Dean. *Benedict Arnold, Military Racketeer.* New York: The Vanguard Press, 1932.

Van Doren, Carl. *Secret History of the American Revolution.* New York: The Viking Press, 1941.

Wallace, Willard M. *Appeal to Arms.* New York: Harper and Brothers, 1951.

——. *Traitorous Hero, The Life and Fortunes of Benedict Arnold.* New York. Harper and Brothers, 1954.

Ward, Christopher: *The War of the Revolution.* New York: The Macmillan Company, 1952.

INDEX

About the Author

JEANNETTE COVERT NOLAN was born in Indiana and has lived there all her life. Her forebears came there as pioneers, and her grandfather owned one of the first newspapers in the state. Her father and brother were newspaper men, and this influenced her to become a writer. On graduation from high school, she worked as a reporter for the Evansville *Courier* until she married. After her children were grown, she turned seriously to writing books, the first of which was published in 1932. Since then she has been very active writing short stories, plays, essays, fiction and biography. She taught creative writing at Indiana University and conducted juvenile workshops at the University of Colorado Writers' Conference. Many of her books have been selected by the Junior Literary Guild, and she was recently voted the outstanding "Hoosier Children's Book Author of the Year."

Nolan, Jeannette Covert
Benedict Arnold

Date Due

SEP 25	MAR 18	JAN 5	
DEC 18	OCT 18	JAN 17	
FEB 28			
MAR 20	MAR 15		
NOV 19	APR 9		
DEC 23	MAR 16		
JAN 19	OCT 13 '8[illegible]		
JAN 28	FEB 14 '84		
MAR 15	NOV 6 '84		
MAR 24	DEC 20		
APR [illegible]	DEC 16		

Describes the main events in the life of this Revolutionary soldier of divided loyalties. Highlights the qualities in his character that caused him to desert the United States and summarizes his years in England.